MW00812549

POPEYE
THE COLLECTIBLE

by Fred Grandinetti

POPEYE is copyrighted by King Features
Syndicate and is used with their permission.

Copyright 1990 Krause Publications, Inc.
All rights reserved. No part of this book may be
reproduced or transmitted in any form or by
any means, electronic or mechanical, including
photocopying, recording, or by any information
storage and retrieval system without the
permission in writing from the Publisher.

Published by:

krause
publications

700 E. State St., Iola, WI 54990
Telephone: (715) 445-2214

Library of Congress Catalog Number: 90-60579
ISBN: 0-87341-143-9
Printed in the United States of America

ABOUT THE AUTHOR:

Fred M. Grandinetti has been a Popeye fan since the age of three. He has been a serious collector since 1983. Fred has had his article/artwork on Popeye published in "Amazing Heroes", "Animato", "Yesterdaze Toys", "Comics Revue", "Model & Toy Shop" and newspapers; "The Watertown Press", "The Watertown Sun", "The news Tribune", "The Middlesex News" and "The Titusville Herald". Fred has taught both children and adults how to draw popular cartoon characters and appeared on children's programs; "The Willie Whistle Show" and "Bozo's Kid's Club".

Fred lives with his family in Watertown, MA.

TABLE OF CONTENTS

ACKNOWLEDGEMENTS

Pat Klug of Krause Publications
Ita Golzman at King Features Syndicate
The Licensing/Publicity Departments at King Features Syndicate
Bill Maling
Gary Matheson
Steve Higgins
Jackson Beck, the voice of "Bluto"/"Brutus"
Jeff Melton
Barry I. Grauman
Dan Mariano
Peter Rizzo for his camera work
Detective Parker Bailey for his developing
Yesterdaze Toys Magazine
Janice Smith
The office staff at the Van Keuren Corporation
Mike and Debbie Brooks, fellow Popeye collectors, and who are organizing a "Popeye Fan Club". Anyone interested in joining, contact the author through the publisher.

..to my friends and relatives who have put up with my interest in the one-eyed sailor all these years. To my family; Dolores, Dom, Dominic and Amy Grandinetti who get up early in the morning being forced to listen to Popeye cartoons and end up going to bed in the evening listening to Popeye cartoons.

INTRODUCTION

Over the past six years I have often been interviewed concerning my interest in Popeye. One question that keeps being asked is, "Why do you admire Popeye so much?" I suppose I respect the sailor because he never expected or wanted anything in return for the good deeds he performed (even if he was saving Olive Oyl from Bluto for the 750th time). As the sailor simply puts it, "I saw my duty and done it". During my school years, I was forever being picked on by students who didn't share my interests in art, theatre, music and cartooning. I would arrive home from school depressed, and wondered if I should give up the interests I enjoyed. However, a few minutes after watching a Popeye cartoon or playing with a Popeye collectible, would quickly cheer me up!

Like many people who collect Popeye collectibles, I had hundreds as a child. The collectibles never stayed in good condition for very long and I find great pleasure in re-collecting the same material I had as a kid. Never did I think that a Popeye coloring book I once purchased for 29¢ as a ten-year-old would cost me $25.00 in 1989! BLOW ME DOWN! I have chosen to focus on Popeye collectibles from the 1950's to 1980's in this publication because material prior to the 1950's has been mentioned often in other publications. I hope by looking at these collectibles you will rediscover those fond memories you had playing with your Popeye collectibles!

COPYRIGHT & COLLECTIBLES

Often, a dealer will price a piece based on the date of the collectible. The dealer will get the date of the item by looking at the object's copyright notice. In Popeye's case, many items feature a © 1929 by King Features Syndicate copyright notice. The item could have been produced in 1955, however, but because Popeye was created (and put under copyright in 1929) the 1929 date will appear as part of the copyright notice on the item. When purchasing a Popeye item do not assume that the 1929 copyright date means the collectible was actually produced in that year.

I had an occasion where my knowledge of Popeye's various character designs came in handy. A dealer was selling a Popeye peanut butter jar and billed the piece as being "SCARCE, 1931". The price of the jar was high, based on the 1931 date. However an illustration of Popeye from the Famous Studios cartoons was pictured on the label. This told me right away that the jar was not from 1931 and was an item produced in the late 1950's due to the popularity Popeye theatre films were having on television. After I gave this information to the dealer, the price was adjusted. The dealer got the 1931 date from a "31" figure stamped on the jar.

If you're planning to collect a great deal of material on any cartoon/comic strip character, I strongly suggest that you do a little research on the character first. In Popeye's case, it'll save you the trouble of paying big money for a piece you thought was sixty years old-only to learn it's merely twenty.

A Popeye Peanut Butter Jar from the late 1950's, produced due to the success the Fleischer/Famous Studios Popeye cartoons were having on television. There is a "31" stamped on the jar which led the dealer who sold this to me to believe that the jar was from 1931, however, Popeye's sailor's uniform told me otherwise! Value: $20.00-$25.00

THE ORIGIN OF POPEYE THE SAILOR

Popeye the Sailor's origin goes back to 1919 and the creation of the comic strip, "Thimble Theatre". "Thimble Theatre" was created by E.C. Segar and starred The Oyl Family: Castor Oyl, his sister Olive, and Olive's then boyfriend, Ham Gravy. On January 17th, 1929, Castor was searching the docks looking for a sailor to run his ship. He came across a fat-forearmed, pipe-smoking fellow and asked him, "Hey there are you a sailor?" "Ja' think I'm a cowboy?", the fellow replied . . . and with that one sentence Popeye the sailor was born.

Pictured is how Popeye first looked when he debuted in Segar's "Thimble Theatre" comic strip on January 17th, 1929.

Segar had only intended to use Popeye in one story and then drop the character. The newspaper reading public fell in love with Popeye's antics and Segar soon made the one-eyed spinach eater the star of the comic strip. Popeye was a character who stood up for what he believed in and spoke his mind. These were traits that the public respected and admired. One must remember that the country was in a deep depression at this time and what the reading public saw Popeye do, they wanted to partake in. Whenever Popeye would show off his super-strength, others were astounded but it never phased Popeye.

If the sailor saw a cat stuck under a house, he'd simply lift the house and free the animal. Popeye never expected or wanted a reward for his actions. Popeye would often stop a battle midstream to remind the audience that he was fighting on the side of right. Segar created quite a supporting cast for Popeye. J.Wellington Wimpy, the classic hamburger moocher, Popeye's adopted son, Swee'pea, The Sea Hag, Popeye's 1st enemy, Alice the Goon, who was the ol' Hag's slave until she beat up the sea-witch and became Swee'pea's babysitter, Geezil, a shoemaker who wanted to see Wimpy dead, Bluto, who became Popeye's main sparring partner in the animated cartoons and Rough House, owner of the diner where Wimpy mooched the majority of his meals. With Popeye the star of "Thimble Theatre", the comic strip was a smashing success appearing in over 600 papers worldwide. By the mid-1930's, Popeye was a well known figure around the globe.

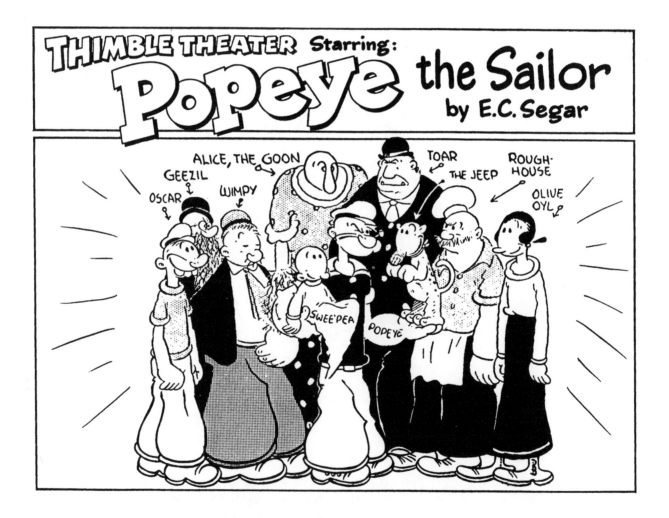

The THIMBLE THEATER Cast

In 1937, Segar was ill for quite some time and wasn't able to draw the strip. So King Features Syndicate's staff artist, Doc Winner drew the art for Segar's scripts. When Segar died in late 1938, Winner continued drawing the strip while Tom Sims handled the writing. In mid-1939 Bela (also known as Bill) Zaboly took over the art work and this team handled the "Thimble Theatre" strip until 1955. In 1955, Sims was replaced by Ralph Stein on the daily writing chores (though he continued on the Sunday strip) and Zaboly continued producing the art. In 1959, Segar's assistant, Bud Sagendorf took over the comic strip. Sagendorf was handling the Popeye comic book while Sims, Zaboly and Stein handled the comic strip. In 1986, Bobby London took over Popeye's comic adventures and it is he who produces the strip today.

Segar's work has been called by many critics as "the Charles Dickens of the comic strip art". In recent years, much of Segar's work has been reprinted for new generations to discover and enjoy.

An example of a Sunday Popeye comic strip at the time the Popeye theatre-produced films were fast on their way to becoming the number one children's TV program in the country. The strip is dated 9-29-57, written by Tom Sims and drawn by Bill (also known as Bela) Zaboly.

Popeye with the sailor's knot around his neck (standing pose) is from the 1960-61 King Features TV version of the spinach-eating sailor.

Popeye's girlfriend, Olive Oyl, first appeared in the comic strip, "Thimble Theatre" in 1919. Olive disliked Popeye at first, but, later grew to adore the sailor man. Olive is as well known around the world as Popeye. Pictured are two 1974 Olive Oyl magnets. The one on the left is the comic strip version of Olive and the one on the right is the King Features TV cartoon (1960-61) version of the character. Ignore the wavy lines in Olive's hair. For the TV cartoons her hair was black. Note the difference in the character's facial design.

J. Wellington Wimpy first appeared in the comic strip in the early 1930's. He went unnamed for a while but was later dubbed, "J. Wellington Wimpy". Wimpy is not a stupid character for it takes alot of creativity to figure ways to mooch hamburgers off of your friends. Wimpy's famous catch-phrase is "I'll gladly pay you Tuesday for a hamburger today". Out of all the characters in the Popeye family who have been animated for film, Wimpy's character design has gone through the LEAST CHANGE. Pictured are two Wimpy magnets. The one on the left is from the comic strip and the one on the right based on the King Features TV cartoons of 1960-61. Both magnets were produced in 1974.

Pictured is Popeye's bearded foe, Brutus. Though Popeye's rival first appeared in the comic strip in 1933, he was called Bluto. It wasn't until production began on the 1960-61 King Features TV cartoons that he was called Brutus. From the mid-1950's to mid-1960's, the character of Popeye's bearded foe went unnamed until the name, "Brutus" was allowed to be used in the print medium as well as film. The Brutus magnets pictured were produced in 1974 and based on the 1960-61 King Features TV version of the character.

© 1983 King Features Syndicate, Inc.
© 1983 Nintendo of America, Inc.

On the left is the comic strip version of The Sea Hag from a POPEYE MAGNET SERIES (1974). On the right is the King Features TV cartoon version (1960-61) of the ol' witch from a playing card produced in 1983 for PARKER BROTHERS' POPEYE CARD GAME.

On the left is Alice the Goon, who debuted in the "Thimble Theatre" comic strip in 1934. She was The Sea Hag's slave when she first appeared but later became Swee'pea's babysitter. Pictured is an Alice the Goon magnet (1974). On the right, is "Patcheye the Pirate" who first appeared in the comic strip in 1971. Pictured is a Patcheye magnet which was incorrectly called "Pegleg" (1974).

On the left is Popeye's father, Poopdeck Pappy. Poopdeck first appeared in the comic strip in 1936. Pappy has quite the temper and thinks nothing of smacking a dame or causing a riot! His temper was toned down for the animated cartoons. Pictured is a Pappy magnet (1974) but it has an error printed on it. Pappy DOES NOT HAVE TATOOS LIKE HIS SON, POPEYE! On the right is one of the Sea Hag's henchmen; "The Evil Spy". Pictured is a "Evil Spy" magnet (1974).

Castor Oyl was the original star of "Thimble Theatre". He is Olive Oyl's brother and first appeared in 1919. When Popeye came along, Castor Oyl was no longer the star of the strip but he has often reappeared. Pictured is a Castor Oyl magnet (1974).

Rough House usually gets his hamburgers mooched by Wimpy in both the comic strip and King Features TV cartoons (1960-61). Rough house has been part of the Popeye family since the early 1930's. Pictured is a Rough house magnet (1974).

Two illustrations of Eugene the magical Jeep from 1960's Popeye collectible cards.

EVIL SPIES

A bunch of Evil Spies, who usuallly do The Sea Hag's biddings, illustrated by Geroge Wildman from the pages of a Popeye comic book.

BLUTO/BRUTUS

A Segar illustration of Bluto/The bully as he appeared in the 1st Fleischer-produced animated cartoon.

The Famous Studios version (in sailor's uniform) of Bluto.

The King Features TV-version of Brutus/The comic strip version of Popeye bumps into the King Features TV-version of Brutus from a 1960's Popeye collectible card/Bud Sagendorf's comic strip version of Brutus.

A Segar illustration of Wimpy's favorite cook.

SEA HAG

3 George Wildman illustrations of the comic strip version of The Sea Hag from the pages of a Popeye comic book.

A Segar illustration of Popeye's pappy (the first time we see his face)/A 1963 illustration of a hot-tempered Pappy.

ALICE THE GOON

A Segar illustration of Alice the Goon caring for Swee'pea/A George Wildman illustration from the pages of a Popeye comic book.

Segar's Wimpy brings a gift to Popeye/The King Features TV version of Wimpy prepares to cook hamburgers. Out of all the characters who have undergone redesigns in the Popeye Family, Wimpy's character design has changed very little.

SWEE'PEA

Segar's Swee'pea playing with Dynamite/a 1960's illustration of Swee'pea from a Popeye Collectible Card.

A Segar illustrated Olive Oyl takes a swing at a monster / Olive takes a fall from a 1960's Popeye Collectible Card/Bud Sagendorf's version of the comic strip version of Olive Oyl (note: Olive's nose is longer and put in the middle of her face).

The Famous Studios version of Olive Oyl with the clump of hair at the top of her forehead and short-sleeved shirt and high-heel shoes. The King Features TV-cartoon version of Olive Oyl has her wearing her comic strip costume but retaining the Famous Studios hairdo.

Popeye takes a stroll with Olive wearing his original hat; his Catain's hat/a George Wildman illustration of Popeye wearing his Captain's hat from the pages of a Popeye comic book.

Popeye did not begin wearing his sailor's hat in the comic strips & comic books until a few years after Bud Sagendorf began drawing the strip. Pictured; An angry Popeye illustrated by George Wildman/a 1963 illustration of Popeye pulling out a can of spinach.

A 1963 illustration of Popeye flying a kite in his white sailor's uniform which he wore in the majority of the Famous Studios /King Features TV-cartoons /Popeye in his white suit from a 1983 playing card by Parker Brothers.

To my pet.

Pictured: the 1950's Famous Studios designs for Olive Oyl and Popeye. Note how Olive has a clump of hair at the top of her forehead, wears a short-sleeved shirt and high heel shoes. This illustration was handled by an animator at Famous Studios and is from a 1961 "POPEYE COLORING BOOK".

"Popeye, what are you doing?"

Pictured: the comic strip designs of Olive Oyl and Popeye from a 1958 "POPEYE COLORING BOOK" illustrated by Popeye comic strip artist, Bill (also known as Bela) Zaboly. I should mention that during the 1960's both the comic strip versions and Famous Studios designs of the Popeye cast were used in the same coloring book. This made the changes in the character's visual design much more apparent.

The King Features TV cartoon version (1960-61) of Popeye prepares to gobble down two cans of spinach. Note: that Popeye is in his white sailor's uniform with a big open eye and large pipe. From KENNER'S SPARKLE PAINT SET (1966).

The King Features TV cartoon version (1960-61) of Olive Oyl looks in her mirror. From KENNER'S SPARKLE PAINT SET (1966).

The King Features TV cartoon version (1960-61) of The Sea Hag has Popeye and Olive locked up in chains! Note The clump of hair at Olive's forehead and open eyes with lashes. These are indications that the illustration is based on the animated cartoon version of Popeye's girlfriend! From KENNER'S SPARKLE PAINT SET (1966).

Pictured are two Popeye slides from Kenner's "Give-A-Show Projector". This is an excellent example of how the animated versions of the Popeye cast influenced Popeye collectibles.

A comic strip/Fleischer Studios version of "Bluto" ties Popeye up in the 1966 slide, "One Track Mind" while the 1960-61 King Features TV design of "Brutus" intends to sink Popeye's boat in the 1962 slide, "Victory At Sea". Often times one company, in this case Kenner toys, would use both the film and strip versions of the Popeye cast for their products. To some this may be confusing but I believe it makes collecting Popeye material much more interesting.

Pictured: A rather strange looking version of Brutus illustrated by George Peed for the 1969 Peter Pan Book and Record Set, "Popeye the Sailor Man. . .A Whale of A Tale".

BLUTO TAGS ALONG

Pictured: A very unusual art-style combination; the comic strip versions of Popeye and Olive Oyl walking alongside the Famous Studios (white uniformed) version of Bluto! From a 1957 Popeye Color and Re-Color Book published by JACK BUILT TOY MANUFACTURING. Illustration drawn by Popeye comic strip artist, Bill (also known as Bela) Zaboly. BLUTO TAGS ALONG

POPEYE GOES FISHING

Pictured: Swee'pea was often seen in a sailor's uniform in the Popeye comic strip from the mid-1950's to 1959. This change in costumes was also reflected in Popeye collectibles from the mid-1950's to mid-1960's. Many illustrations of Swee'pea on coloring books or pencil by number sets featured Swee'pea in his sailor's suit. Illustration by 1957's Popeye Color and Re-Color Book published by JACK BUILT TOY MANUFACTURING. POPEYE GOES FISHING

Several of Popeye records have been produced since the early days of the sailor's creation. Pictured is one of the first records to feature the "I'm Popeye the Sailor Man" theme song recorded by Popeye's cartoon voice, Jack Mercer. Mercer began voicing Popeye in 1935 and handled the character's vocals until his death in 1984. He also voiced Bluto in several Fleischer Studio cartoons, Wimpy in the King Features TV cartoons (1960-61) and all the characters in the 1960's "Felix the Cat" TV-cartoons. Mercer also wrote hundreds of cartoon scripts over the years for Paramount Pictures.

Another characteristic of the animated Popeye of the 1950's-60's features Popeye with two open eyes! The pictured illustration was by an animator at Famous Studios and used in a 1961 "POPEYE COLORING BOOK".

Popeye squares off with a Fleischer Studios/comic strip version of Bluto from Hasbro's 1957 Numbered Coloring Set.

Live hosts often introduced cartoons to their children's audience during the mid-1950's throughout the 1960's. WMUR-TV's "Uncle Gus" show is where I got my first exposure to the Fleischer/Famous Studios Popeye cartoons. Uncle Gus would often crank Mattel Toy's Popeye Jack-In-The Box just before a Popeye film would be shown.

The comic strip version of Popeye warns Wimpy from Hasbro's 1957 Numbered Coloring Set.

A pipe-less Popeye from Hasbro's 1957

Numbered Coloring Set.

POPEYE ON FILM

90.3% OF THE MOST INFLUENTIAL ORGANIZATIONS IN THE COUNTRY*
APPROVED POPEYE FOR CHILDREN ON TV

THEY SAID IT LOUD AND CLEAR!

"PERFECTLY ACCEPTABLE FOR CHILDREN"
—Executive Council Episcopal Church

"ALL CHILDREN WHOM I KNOW LOVE POPEYE"
—Girl Scout Council of New York

"IT'S JUST FUN"
—Archdiocese of New York

"ENTIRELY ACCEPTABLE FOR CHILDREN—EVEN SLIGHTLY EDUCATIONAL"
—NYC Federation of Women's Clubs

"THERE IS NO EVILNESS OR VIOLENCE IN POPEYE CARTOONS"
—Kiwanis Club of New York

AN OVERWHELMING VOTE OF CONFIDENCE FOR
CONFIDENT CHILDREN'S PROGRAMMING

United Artists Television Inc
*Entertainment from
Transamerica Corporation*

30

By the early 1930's, Popeye was heard on NBC radio and collectible toys were appearing in department stores. However, the biggest impression the sailor would have on the public would be in the field of animated cartoons. In 1933, Max Fleischer, who already had success with his "Out of the Inkwell" and "Betty Boop" cartoons, decided that Popeye would make a funny cartoon character. In 1933, Popeye, Olive and Bluto made their animated film debut in a "Betty Boop" cartoon called "Popeye the Sailor". This film was used to test Popeye's popularity in the field of animated films. The Boop cartoon was a huge success and Popeye's own cartoon series shortly followed. From 1933 to 1942, Fleischer produced over 100 Popeye films. By 1938 the Popeye cartoons became more popular with audiences than Walt Disney's Mickey Mouse (this still holds true today). Today, these cartoons are considered classics in the field of animation. In 1942, Fleischer's Studio was taken over by Paramount Picture's new animation studio, Famous Studios. Famous Studios continued production of the Popeye films until 1957 (the year before the majority of the Popeye cartoons had been sold to Associated Artists Productions for television syndication). The Famous Studios Popeye cartoons are usually the films where the plot consists of Bluto and Popeye battling over Olive Oyl. While Popeye wore a sailor's costume closely matching his comic strip outfit in the Fleischer films, both he and Bluto sported Navy whites in the majority of the Famous Studios cartoons.

When the Fleischer and Famous Studios Popeye cartoons debuted on television in 1956 they caused quite a stir. Suddenly an entire new generation of children discovered the animated antics of the one-eyed sailor man and couldn't get enough of his adventures. The Popeye cartoons were so popular that hundreds of new Popeye collectibles popped up due directly to his exposure on the small screen. Many products billed Popeye as "TV's Most Popular Cartoon Star" . . . and they were right. By 1960, Popeye was appearing on over 150 stations and was the most popular animated children's show in the country. King Features Syndicate, who owned the rights to Popeye, decided to supervise the production of 220 TV-produced cartoons for television syndication. By the fall of 1961, 454 Popeye films were airing - making the series the longest running in the history of animated cartoons. Throughout the 1960's, Popeye collectibles continued to appear in stores, due to his success in the film and television mediums.

In 1978, CBS television debuted "The All New Popeye Hour" on Saturday mornings. This series (in various versions) lasted for five years. A follow-up Saturday morning cartoon show was "Popeye & Son" aired on CBS for the 1987-88 season. Today, over 600 Popeye cartoons are syndicated all over the world. In many areas, the films can be seen three or four times a day. In 1989 an average of 70 Popeye cartoons were aired seven days a week in the Boston, MA area. Though Popeye started out as a successful comic strip character, many collectibles were produced due to his enduring popularity in the field of animated cartoons.

THE FLEISCHER STUDIOS (1933-1942). This studio was funded by Paramount Pictures and produced the original, classic Popeye the Sailor cartoons for theatres. When these black & white films debuted on television in 1956, they became a hit with a whole new generation of children and inspired hundreds of new Popeye collectibles. These cartoons have recently been colorized and released for Television syndication.

FAMOUS STUDIOS (1942-1957). Famous Studios, also funded by Paramount Pictures, brought character design changes to the Popeye cast. Though it was the Fleischer Studios which introduced a white sailor suited Popeye to animation, this uniform became a permanent fixture in the Famous Studios films. Bluto also donned a white sailor's uniform in these films. In 1945, Famous Studios, changed Olive's costume and hair-do. All of the mentioned changes affected the Popeye collectibles manufactured in the late 1950's.

A still from the 1956 Famous Studios cartoon, "Assault & Flattery" in which Bluto attempts to sue Popeye for all the beatings he's suffered at the hands of the spinach-eating sailor. "Popeye" cartoons became the most popular children's animated series in the country shortly after their television debut. Another popular children's program, "The Three Stooges", was often paired with Popeye cartoons by many stations throughout the 1960's. This team proved to be a winning combination as many stations aired "Popeye & The Three Stooges" in addition to carrying the two series individually. This still was originally in color and valued at $10.00.

KING FEATURES TELEVISION CARTOONS (1960-61). Because the Fleischer/Famous Studios Popeye cartoons were so popular on television, King Features Syndicate, who own the rights to Popeye, decided to produce a new series of Popeye cartoons for television. Several studios produced the films under the "King Features TV Syndicate" banner; Larry Harmon, Gerald Ray, Jack Kinney, Gene Deitch & William Snyder and Paramount Cartoon Studios. Popeye still wore his white uniform in these cartoons. Bluto was now called Brutus and wore a short-sleeved shirt with big buttons. Olive, while still wearing her new Famous Studios hair-do, was back in her original comic strip costume. After the release of these Popeye cartoons in the fall of 1961, many collectibles used the King Features TV cartoon designs of the cast on several collectibles.

HANNA BARBERA'S POPEYE (1978-1983). Popeye made his Saturday morning cartoon debut in 1978 with CBS' "All New Popeye Hour". The Popeye character designs were pretty close to the comic strip designs and a few collectibles were based on Hanna Barbera illustrations.

HANNA BARBERA'S "POPEYE & SON" (1987-88). This series of cartoons featured Popeye's blond haired son, "Junior". Popeye now wore a flowered shirt with blue cap and Olive sported a funky hair-do. There have been several Popeye collectibles produced based on "Popeye & Son".

234 cartoons - Fleischer/Famous Studios
220 cartoons - King Features TV cartoons
192 segments from "All New Popeye Hour" & sequels
13 "Popeye & Son" half hours — The "Popeye" film series is currently the longest running produced in the history of animated cartoons.

After the Popeye animated cartoons debuted on television in 1956, many collectibles were based on the animated versions of Popeye and his friends rather than the more established comic strip designs. The animated products are rare among dealer tables today and they are what I concentrate on when purchasing Popeye material for my collection. Here is a guide for knowing what item is based on the comic strip versions of the Popeye cast and animated versions:

ANIMATED GUIDE

Always check the date. A product based on the animated version of the Popeye cast will probably be either from the mid-1950's to mid-1970's.

Popeye will be wearing his white sailor's suit with a white circle around his eye. His corn-cob pipe will look bigger than usual and his pant legs will look smoother than usual. In many products, Popeye's white sailor's uniform will be colored light blue (dolls for example).

Olive Oyl will either be wearing her Famous Studios costume (a short-sleeved shirt and striped black blouse) or her comic strip costume. One thing that will be the same for the animated version of Olive Oyl is her hair-do. If Olive has a clump of hair at the top of her forehead, then it is the animated cartoon design of Popeye's girlfriend.

Bluto and Brutus are the tricky ones to watch. If Bluto appears in a white sailor's uniform, then this is the animated version of Popeye's foe. I have only seen this design used on three Popeye collectibles so I don't consider it very common. Brutus was the name given to Popeye's foe during the 1960-61 TV cartoons produced by King Features Syndicate. He is the same character as Bluto but he dresses differently. The animated version of Brutus dresses in a button down the front blue shirt which makes his belly stick out. His pants are smooth looking and his big feet stick out. The shirt Brutus wears is short-sleeved with a open neckline. Brutus also appears to have a fuller beard than the animated Bluto version.

The Sea Hag, another of Popeye's foes, wasn't used very often except on a few pieces. The character appeared often in the 1960-61 TV cartoons and a few Popeye collectibles. The Hag's animated design features her with a long chin and nose. Usually, one or two thin hairs are seen protruding from the hood she wears around her head.

ANIMATION COLLECTIBLES

As of this writing, at least four different television stations, which can be picked up in the Boston, MA area, carry the animated adventures of Popeye. For the rating period ending in April 1989, the Popeye films were rated the 4th most popular animated children's program by the A.C. Nielsen Co. Popeye edged out "Teenage Mutant Ninja Turtles", one of the current cartoon crazes. Ever since Popeye's television debut in 1956, the one-eyed sailor has enjoyed overwhelming popularity on television. With all the success the Popeye cartoons have had, one would think that there is a great deal of material used in the actual production of a Popeye cartoon, to collect! However, there are few Popeye animation collectibles to be found and any that are located usually command high prices.

When the original Popeye films were being produced for the movie screen, no one who worked on the cartoons saved any production material. Who would have thought a pencil sketch or animation cel would have any value back in the early days of the animated cartoon? Animated cartoons were only considered "short-subjects" (popular as they were) so space wasn't provided to store any production material which was used to create the cartoons. Today an animation cel or production drawing from the Fleischer Studios, featuring a Popeye character, can cost as high as $300.00. A production drawing of Olive Oyl from a Fleischer cartoon was valued at $150.00 by The Cricket Gallery, who specialize in selling animation art. A line drawing of Popeye from the Fleischer film, "Popeye Meets William Tell" (1940) was selling for $195.00 at The Gallery Lainzberg a few years back. Popeye cartoons which were produced by Famous Studios also command high prices for animation cels or production drawings. A production drawing of Popeye, Olive and Bluto from the 1949 Famous Studios film, "Silly Hillbilly" was selling for $125.00 at The Gallery Lainzberg.

If you are lucky enough to obtain any material used in producing a Popeye cartoon . . . hold on to it! As new generations discover the popularity of the over 600 Popeye cartoons in television syndication, the price of each animation collectible is sure to increase.

Copy of a figure of Popeye taken from an animation cel originally in color from a 1970's Popeye cartoon produced in Europe. It is signed by animators, Dan Hunn and Ron Fritz. Value: $95.00.

A production drawing of Popeye, Olive & Bluto used during the making of the Famous Studios cartoon "Beaus Will Be Beaus". Though the drawing is dated March 13th, 1953 the copyright date on the actual cartoon is 1955. Value: $160.00.

Copy of a figure of Popeye in his white sailor's uniform taken from an animation cel originally in color used during the filming of the 1972 Industrial film, "Look Where You Are Going" for King Features Syndicate. Value: $175.00.

Many Popeye collectibles from the late 1950's made reference to the sailor's film career. Pictured is the back of a Popeye record sleeve from the late 1950's. It was produced by Associated Artists Productions (A.A.P.), who was the television syndicator of the Fleischer/Famous Studios films for several years. Note how the record is billed as "Official Popeye TV Record Album" and features a Famous Studios version of Bluto's face. The actual value of the record is $10.00.

A copy of a figure of Olive Oyl taken from a color animation cel used for the 1978-83 Hanna Barbera Popeye cartoons. Value: $40.00.

A copy of a figure of Bluto taken from a color animation cel used for the 1978-83 Hanna Barbera Popeye cartoons. Value: $40.00.

Pictured is a still, originally in color, of the 1978-83 Hanna Barbera versions of Popeye and The Sea Hag seen while Hanna Barbera was producing "The All New Popeye Hour"/"Popeye and Olive Comedy Show" programs for Saturday morning television. Value: $5.00.

A copy of a figure of Popeye taken from a color animation cel used for the 1978-83 Hanna Barbera Popeye cartoons. Value: $50.00.

Box to "Popeye & His Pals" Candy/Toy product by PHOE-
NIX CANDY CO. from the mid-1960's. The illustration of
Popeye's face was probably taken from an animation cel as it
was lifted directly from the 1960 Jack Kinney-produced King
Features TV cartoon, "Sea Hagracy". Value: $10.00-$15.00
(Box courtesy of Mike & Debbie Brooks).

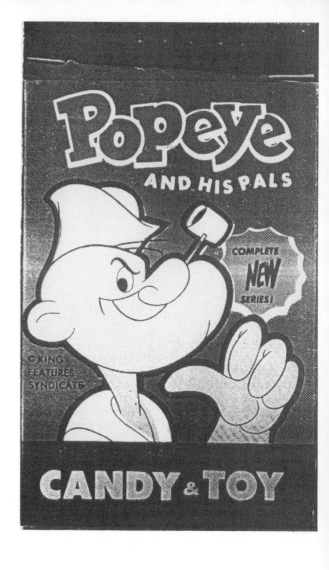

Back of the "Popeye & His Pals" Candy/Toy product by
PHOENIX CANDY CO. On the back of each box featured a
color by numbers drawing. Pictured are Popeye and the King
Features TV version of The Sea Hag. The illustration of the
pair was probably taken from an animation cel as it is
directly lifted from the 1960 Jack Kinney-produced King
Features TV cartoon, "Sea Hagracy".

COMIC BOOK COLLECTIBLES

Popeye the Sailor began his long comic book career in the pages of David McKay's "KING COMICS" in 1936. "King Comics" featured King Features Syndicate comic strip characters. All the strips seen in the book was first published in Sunday/Daily comic sections. The Popeye Family were always featured on the cover of all 159 issues. Early issues of "King Comics" featured strip reprints by Popeye's creator, E.C. Segar, but the majority of the work reprinted was done by Bela Zaboly (art) and Tom Sims (writer).

Popeye strip reprints by Zaboly & Sims also appeared in two other David McKay publications; "Ace Comics" & "Magic Comics".

The first Popeye comic book was published in 1948 by Dell Comics. The material was done by Popeye cartoonist Bud Sagendorf, who took over the comic strip in 1959. Gold Key comics took over the series starting with issue No. 66. King Features Syndicate formed their own comic book publishing co. called, "King Comics" and took over the Popeye series beginning with issue No. 81. Charlton Comics took over the comic book adventures of Popeye starting with issue No. 94. The art work for the majority of the Charlton issues was provided by George Wildman. It's interesting to note that Wildman began drawing the comic strip version of Brutus then later switched to the King Features TV version. He later switched back to the comic strip design.

Gold Key resumed publication of Popeye starting with issue 139 and Whitman carried on beginning with No. 156. Whitman discontinued its line of comic books, and production ceased on any new Popeye material with issue No. 171. However, "Ocean Comics" started producing special Popeye stories based on revamping Popeye's comic strip origins in 1987.

Any comic book material featuring Segar's work is very costly in value. Depending upon their condition, Segar art "King Comics" can cost as high as $1610. Charlton Popeye issues can value from $5.00-$7.00 as time passes. It should be mentioned that King Features Syndicate used Popeye in comic book form for 15 Educational Comics. Though these comics were originally give-a-ways, they now are being sold as back issues among many comic book dealers. Popeye was featured in his white sailor suit in many of these issues.

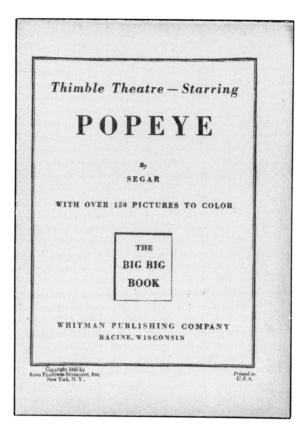

While this publication deals with Popeye collectibles from the 1950's-1980's it should be noted that Popeye material featuring art by E. C. Segar is of great value. Pictured is a page from a 1935 Big Little Book illustrated by Segar and published by WHITMAN PUBLISHING COMPANY.

A Segar illustration from a 1935 Popeye Big Little Book. Note Segar's trademark signature at lower right hand side.

A "Thimble Theatre" strip as it appeared in "King Comics" No. 81, 1943. By Tom Sims & Bela Zaboly.

This strip (companion-piece) to "Thimble Theatre" during the 1930's-1940's was called "Sappo". Often times the characters of Sappo and Prof. O. G. WottaSnozzle were featured on Popeye collectibles of the 1950's-60's. Pictured is a strip reprint which appeared in "King Comics" No. 81 (1943) by Tom Sims and Bela Zaboly.

Pictured, an ad from the pages of "King Comics" featuring Popeye as spokesperson.

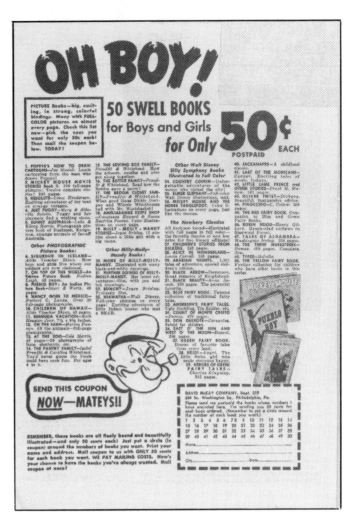

"Popeye The Sailor-Sea Stories" published by GOLD KEY (1962). Featured on the cover, from top to bottom are, Sea Hag's pet vulture, Alice the Goon, Wimpy, Olive, Poopdeck Pappy, Popeye, Eugene the Jeep, Granny (Popeye's Grandmother), Geezil, Swee'pea and The Sea Hag. Value: $10.00-$20.00 (a GIANT SIZED ISSUE). Cover art by Bud Sagendorf.

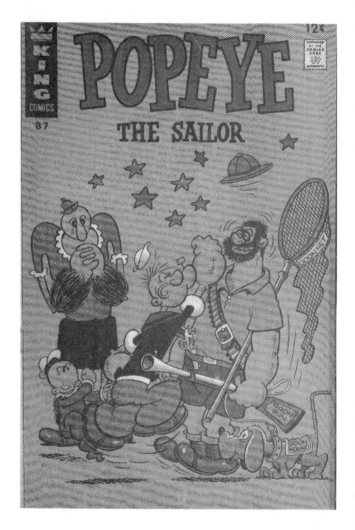

"*Popeye the Sailor*" *No. 87 published by KING COMICS (1967). Popeye punches the comic strip/comic book version of Brutus with Swee'Pea and Alice the Goon by his side. Value: $5.00-$3.00. Cover art by Bud Sagendorf.*

"*Popeye the Sailor*" *No. 108 published by CHARLTON COMICS (1971). This was a special issue featuring "The Story of Popeye" (very distorted, however). Value: $3.00-$5.00. Cover art by George Wildman.*

"Popeye the Sailor" No. 122 published by CHARLTON COMICS (1973). Popeye re-introduces "Toar" to the family. "Toar" is a 20,000 year old caveman who first appeared in the "Thimble Theatre" strip in the early 1930's. When he first debuted he was the servant of The Sea Hag's sister. Value: $3.00-$5.00. Cover art by George Wildman.

"Popeye and Communications and Media Careers" published by KING COMICS (1972). One in a series of career guide comic books featuring Popeye in either his comic strip costume or white sailor's uniform. Value: $2.00-$1.00. Cover art by Ray Dirgo.

"Popeye the Sailor" No. 144 published by GOLD KEY (1979). Popeye celebrates his 50th Anniversary in this special issue. Pictured on the cover are Olive, Swee'pea, Wimpy, Brutus, Poopdeck Pappy and Prof. O. G. WottaSnozzle. Value: $5.00-$2.00. Cover art by George Wildman.

"Popeye-Borned To The Sea!" published by OCEAN COMICS (1987). In this special issue, Popeye was illustrated less cartoony. Featured on the cover, from top left to bottom right: Poopdeck Pappy, Brutus, Dan O Mite, Roxy (Popeye's mom), Wimpy & WattaSnozzle. Value: $2.00-$5.00. Cover artist unknown.

"Popeye's Pen Pal" from an issue of CHARLTON's "Popeye" comic book series. Question two gives a wrong answer, however, concerning Swee'pea's name. Though his correct name is "Swee'pea", he has been called "Sweetpea" in many collectibles over the years.

A sequence from one of the Career Guide Comic books featuring Popeye and Swee'pea. Art by Ray Dirgo.

Pictured: George Wildman's comic strip version of Brutus illustrated in "Popeye the Sailor" No. 95 (1969) published by CHARLTON COMICS.

Pictured: George Wildman's King Features TV-cartoon style of Brutus illustrated in "Popeye the Sailor" No. 115 (1972) published by CHARLTON COMICS. Wildman began illustrating the comic strip version of Brutus, switched to the 1960-61 TV-cartoon style and then went back to the comic strip design.

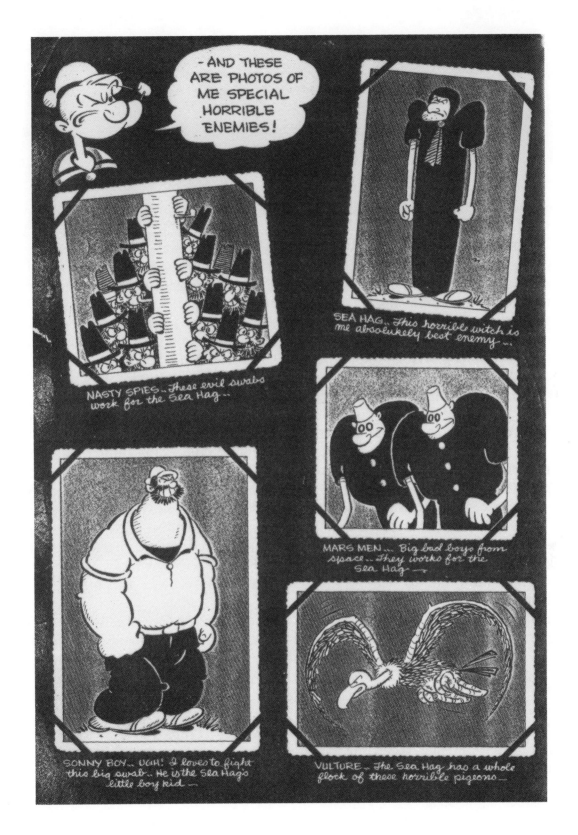

Pictured: Popeye's 1959 Rogue's Gallery! Note how the bearded bully is called "Sonny Boy" though he looks just like Bluto! Because of a copyright conflict, Bud Sagendorf could not call Popeye's fat rival "Bluto" for a period in the Popeye comic books he wrote/illustrated. By the mid-1960's, however, Sagendorf was allowed to call him "Brutus" the name used in the King Features TV-cartoons of 1960-61.

COMIC BOOK NAME GAME

Popeye often battled a bully who looked like the comic strip/Fleischer Studios version of Bluto in the Popeye comic books from the 1950's to mid-1960's. It was around the 1966/67 Popeye comic book stories that this brute became known as "Brutus" in print. The character who looked like Bluto was often billed as "The Sea Hag's Son-Sonny Boy" or he simply went unnamed. The character wasn't called Bluto because of a copyright dispute over the origin of the character's name. Jackson Beck, who provided the voice for Bluto in the majority of the color Famous Studios cartoons and Brutus for the 1960-61 King Features TV cartoons informed me that Bluto was a late character introduced in the films, and the name "Bluto" was under the ownership of Paramount Pictures, who financed the Fleischer Studio/Famous Studios Popeye films. When King Features Syndicate decided to produce animated cartoons for television in 1960-61, the only character's name they supposedly didn't already have under copyright was "Bluto". King Features Syndicate changed the bully's name to "Brutus" for their 220 TV cartoons.

What throws this suggestion of the name change out of whack is the fact that the character of Bluto first appeared in Segar's "Thimble Theatre" comic strip in 1932. NOT in the animated cartoons. The character of Bluto also appeared in the comic strip of the 1950's as well as Popeye collectibles during this period. Both the strips and collectibles are all copyrighted © KING FEATURES SYNDICATE, leading one to believe that the name "Bluto" was also under their ownership.

Mr. Beck mentioned that he wasn't sure if the name change actually had to do with a copyright dispute, but he believed that this was the information given to him. The fact remains, as far as collectibles are concerned, Popeye's bearded rival for the affections of Olive Oyl has gone by two names in Popeye merchandise since 1960. The actual reason for the name change may continue to remain a mystery. Another reason for the change in name which has been mentioned is that Walt Disney felt "Bluto" sounded too much like "Pluto", Mickey's dog.

As Popeye would sing regarding the change in his rival's name: "Whatever his name . . He's always a pain . . to Popeye the Sailor Man" . . . . . TOOT! TOOT!

ILLUSTRATION HISTORY

On many Popeye collectibles of the 1930's, Popeye's creator E.C. Segar did the artwork for many products. This has made these early pieces very costly. During the 1940's, Bud Sagendorf, who later took over the Popeye comic strip and produced the Popeye comic books for several years, provided the artwork for Popeye related merchandise. Sagendorf and King Features' staff artist, Joe Musial, provided much of the artwork on Popeye collectibles of the 1940's. During the 1950's, Sagendorf and fellow Popeye comic strip artist, Bill (also known as Bela) Zaboly handled the art chores on Popeye merchandise. Zaboly's art could be seen on many Popeye collectibles produced due to the popularity the theatre Popeye cartoons were having on television. Publicity stills which King Features Syndicate used to promote their Popeye television cartoons of 1960-61 often were used as art work on Popeye collectibles throughout the 1960's.

During the 1970's to present day, King Features Syndicate provided to companies producing Popeye items, a series of illustrations of the Popeye cast in various poses. The manufacturer would then give these drawings to their staff artists to illustrate appropriate poses. Often, illustrations were taken directly from the material King Features Syndicate supplied and put on the product. This explains why you may see the same illustration of Popeye pictured on several different collectibles.

NEWSPAPER COLLECTIBLES

Another type of Popeye collectible is the collection of original daily or Sunday Popeye comic strips. There are many dealers across the country who collect and sell original comic sections. If you're lucky enough to find a dealer who sells Segar artwork the price tag could be staggering! However, Popeye comic strips from the 1950's-60's are not that costly. Material by Tom Sims, Ralph Stein, Bill Zaboly and Bud Sagendorf often has a price tag of no more than $7.00. Collecting a Popeye daily comic strip and understanding what's happening can be a problem. While the Sunday strip was a complete story the daily strip featured on-going adventures.

There appears to be more and more dealers who will display and sell original comic strip artwork.

A copy of an original pencil drawing used for the 5-20-58 "Thimble Theatre" daily strip by Ralph Stein and Bill Zaboly. Value of the complete strip: $75.00.

A copy of an original pencil drawing used for the 5-21-58 "Thimble Theatre" daily strip by Ralph Stein and Bill Zaboly. Value of the complete set: $75.00.

A "Thimble Theatre" Sunday page taken directly from a Sunday comics section on 7-14-57 by Tom Sims and Bill Zaboly. Featured in this strip is Oscar, Swee'pea's buck-toothed pal, who was used in many Popeye collectibles illustrated by Bill Zaboly during the late 1950's. Value of the strip (in original form): $7.00.

For CRYIN' Out Loud!

Olive Oyl's bawling so strenuously because E. C. Segar won't give her time out to read his famous comic in which she acts—

Thimble Theatre
Starring the Celebrated POPEYE

Don't miss this sidesplitting comic.

Read it every day in the

WISCONSIN NEWS

POPEYE the tough old salt who uses carbolic acid to flavor his drinks . . . bullets can't penetrate his rhinoceros skin. A smacking . . . walloping . . . smashing cartoon that's funny even without words! After one round of laughs at this unique comic you'll want to follow it . . .

Daily in the

WISCONSIN NEWS

Pictured: Two newspaper ads from the early 1930's promoting Segar's "Thimble Theatre" strip.

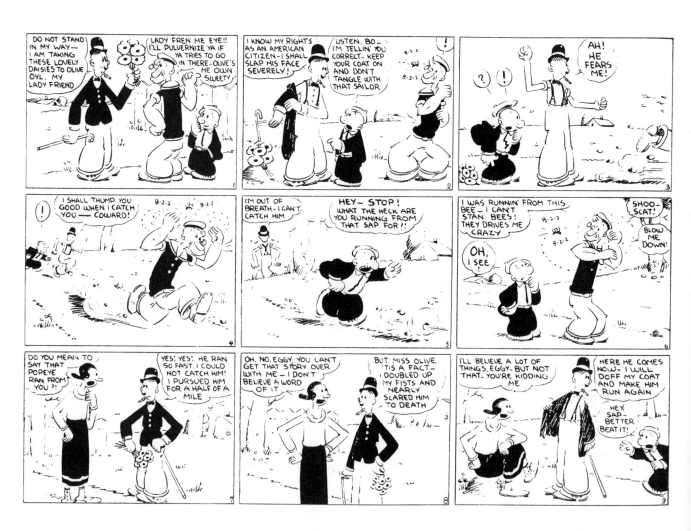

Pictured: A portion of a "Thimble Theatre" strip as described in a catalog for sale to collectors.

BOOKS/COLORING BOOKS

The Samuel Lowe Co. produced several Popeye coloring, activity, dot to dot and sticker fun books from the late 1950's to mid 1960's. Many books billed Popeye by mentioning his booming popularity as a TV cartoon star. The covers to these books featured excellent artwork while the illustrations inside were handled by either longtime Popeye comic strip cartoonists' Bill Zaboly and Bud Sagendorf, or by animators who worked at Paramount Pictures' cartoon studio, Famous Studios. It is important for collectors to know that while different cover designs were used on each book, many of the illustrations inside were often repeated in other coloring books. This appears to be a longstanding practice in the coloring book field.

Whitman Publishing later printed Popeye coloring books as well as Big Little Books. Recently Golden Books has taken over publication of any new Popeye coloring books which have appeared. The artwork in the Whitman/Golden material has been by artists who the publishing firms employ.

Wonder Books, a trademark of Grosset & Dunlap Inc., has published many Popeye story books since the 1950's. Titles in this series include, "Popeye", "Popeye Goes On A Picnic", "Popeye's Big Surprise", "The House That Popeye Built", "Popeye Goes Fishing", "Popeye and The Haunted House" and "Popeye Climbs a Mountain". Many of these books have had several printings and can still be bought in stores today. Popeye's adventures have also been translated into other languages. In Italy, for example, Popeye has had his own Italian-language comic book series.

Popeye coloring book #2925 (1958) published by BONNIE BOOKS/CHILD CRAFT SERIES/SAMUEL LOWE CO. One of the earliest Popeye coloring books produced due to the success of the Popeye theatre cartoons on television. Note how Popeye is swinging at a Fleischer Studio/comic strip version of Bluto and Swee'pea is wearing a sailor's uniform. He was often seen in the Popeye comic strip from the mid-1950's to 1959. Value: $25.00

The back of Popeye coloring book #2925 (1958) promoting, "TV's Most Popular Stars".

Popeye coloring book #2945 (1958) published by BONNIE BOOKS/CHILD CRAFT SERIES/SAMUEL LOWE CO. The cover features the comic strip versions of Popeye and Olive Oyl. Value: $25.00

Popeye coloring book #2834 (1959) published by THE SAMUEL LOWE CO. Note how Popeye is billed on the front of this coloring book as "TV's MOST POPULAR CARTOON STAR" and that the sailor is pictured sitting in a TV SCREEN. This is a clear indication that the book is based on the popularity of the Popeye animated cartoons. Value: $25.00

Popeye coloring book #2834 (1961) published by THE SAMUEL LOWE CO. The character designs of Popeye, Olive, Wimpy, Swee'pea and Brutus are all based on the 1960-61 King Features TV cartoons. Note that the book is billed as "TV'S FAVORITE POPEYE AND HIS TV CARTOON PALS." Value: $25.00

Popeye coloring book #4924 (1961) published by THE SAMUEL LOWE CO. One of Popeye's nephews (from the Famous Studios cartoons) is featured playing a horn on the cover along with the Famous Studios/King Features TV cartoon design of Popeye featured on the right side of the book the comic strip version of Popeye is holding. The Famous Studios design of Olive's head is featured on the left side of the book above Wimpy. Note how the book is billed as "FAVORITE TV CARTOON CHARACTERS TO COLOR .. SUPER BOOK". This publication featured both the comic strip and Famous Studios designs of the Popeye cast. Value: $25.00

Popeye Secret Pictures #3097 (1962) published by THE SAMUEL LOWE CO. This was a connect-the-dot book featuring the King Features TV cartoon (1960-61) version of Popeye on the cover. The illustrations inside were based on both the King Features TV designs and Famous Studios versions. Value: $25.00

Popeye Complete Activity Book #2831 (1960) published by THE SAMUEL LOWE CO. The Famous Studios designs were used in this book despite the fact the comic strip versions were illustrated on the front. Note on the cover how it states, "WATCH POPEYE CARTOONS ON TV". Value: $30.00

Popeye Sticker Book #2631 (1961) published by THE SAMUEL LOWE CO. The Famous Studios versions of the Popeye cast were featured in this book though the comic strip designs of Popeye and Swee'pea are on the cover. Note how the words "TV STAR" are above "Popeye". Value $30.00

Popeye's punch out/sticker fun book #2631 (1962) published by THE SAMUEL LOWE CO. The comic strip designs of the Popeye cast were featured in this book. Value: $30.00

Popeye Sticker Fun #2631 (1963) published by THE SAMUEL LOWE CO. The cover shows the King Features TV cartoon version of Popeye popping out of the book while the comic strip design of Olive holds down the left hand side of the book. The Famous Studios designs were illustrated inside. Value: $30.00

Popeye coloring book #939 (1963) published by THE SAMUEL LOWE CO. The Famous Studios designs were illustrated in the book while the comic strip versions were drawn on the cover. Swee'pea again wears the sailor's uniform he frequently was seen in in the Popeye comic strip from the mid-1950's to 1959. Value: $15.00-$20.00 (this is a very thin book)

Popeye color-by-numbers #2959E (1963) published by THE SAMUEL LOWE CO. The comic strip designs of Olive and Wimpy watch Swee'pea color in the King Features TV version of Popeye on the cover. This book has an interesting mix of comic strip/Famous Studios/King Features TV cartoon illustrations pictured inside. Value: $25.00

Popeye connect-the-dot/color-by-numbers #3097 (1963) published by THE SAMUEL LOWE CO. The King Features TV designs of Popeye rides a horse on the cover. Pictured inside are Famous Studios designs. Popeye shared this book with "KRAZY KAT" though the feline is not mentioned on the cover. Value: $25.00

Popeye is featured in FOUR TELEVISION SHOW FAVORITES COLORING BOOK #4952 (1964) published by THE SAMUEL LOWE CO. Along with Popeye are Beetle Bailey, Snuffy Smith and Barney Google and Krazy Kat. Value: $25.00

Popeye coloring book #2834 (1964) featuring the comic strip designs of the Popeye cast illustrated inside and the King Features TV cartoon version of Popeye sailing a ship on the front. Published by THE SAMUEL LOWE CO. Note how the book is billed as "TV COLORING BOOK". Value: $25.00

Popeye Dot-to-Dot Book #1062-65 (1978) published by GOLDEN BOOKS. The comic strip Popeye cast takes a trip around the globe. Value: $5.00

Popeye coloring book #1062-54 (1978) published by GOLDEN BOOKS. The illustrations inside are based on the comic strip designs of the Popeye cast. The story, "Swee'pea discovers a giant egg", is taken from a 1960's Popeye comic book story. Value: $5.00

Popeye coloring book #1045-52 (1979) published by GOLDEN BOOKS. The comic strip version of Popeye takes a "Funtime Fiesta". Value: $5.00

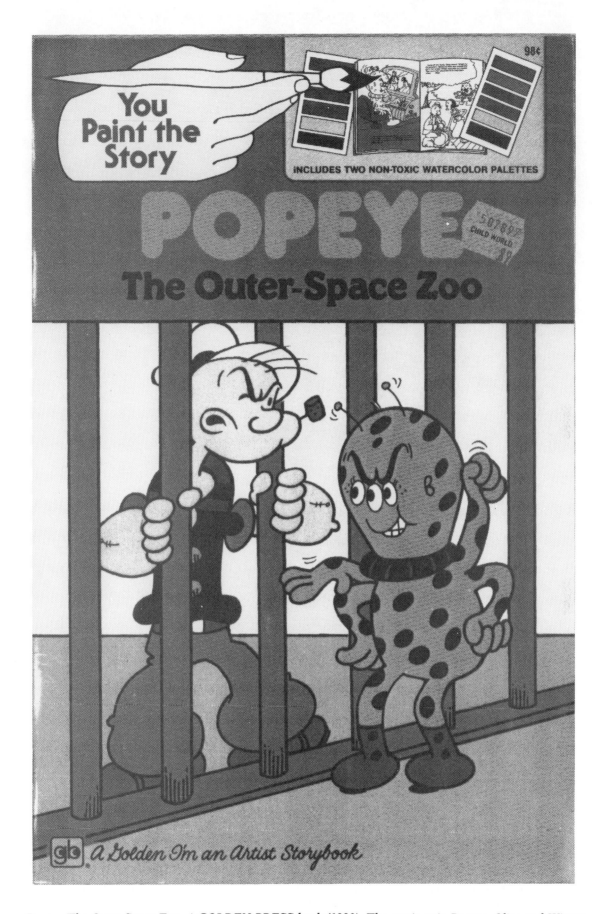

Popeye-The Outer Space Zoo. A GOLDEN PRESS book (1980). The comic strip Popeye, Olive and Wimpy battle an alien menace. Value: $5.00-$7.00

Popeye coloring book #1833-40 (1981) published by GOLDEN BOOKS. The comic strip cast is featured in two stories. The 1st features Popeye and Brutus' search for Lil' Swee'pea while Wimpy stars in the second, titled, "A Fella Needs A Grill".

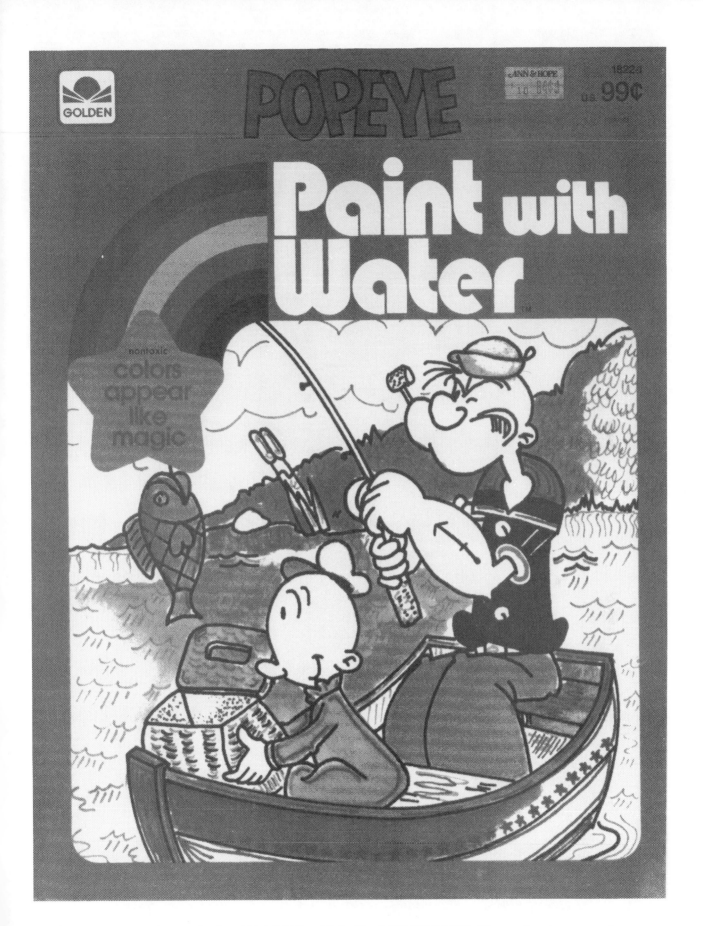

Popeye paint with water book #1822-1 (1981) published by GOLDEN BOOKS. The comic strip cast travels to other lands. Value: $3.00

Popeye coloring book #1045-51 (1982) published by GOLDEN BOOKS. The story featuring the comic strip cast is "Popeye and The Spinach Stalk". Value: $3.00

Popeye-Ghost Ship To Treasure Island (1967) published by WHITMAN PUBLISHING CO. Story by Paul S. Newman. This was a Big Little Book featuring an exciting tale of Poopdeck Pappy's search for a lost treasure. Value: $5.00-$10.00

Popeye-Deep Sea Danger (1980) published by WHITMAN PUBLISHING CO. Story by Paul S. Newman. Popeye and his crew battle sea monsters and a hypnotist! A Big Little Book adventure. Value: $3.00

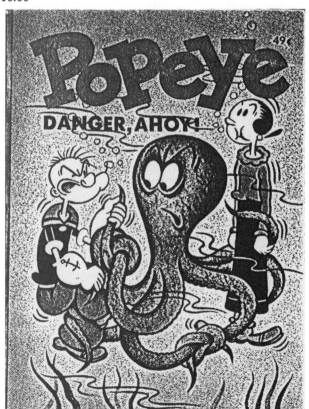

Popeye-Queen Olive Oyl (1973) published by WHITMAN PUBLISHING CO. This Big Little Book adventure was actually a remake of a 1941 story where Olive becomes Queen of the Kingdom, Olivoyla! This book also featured a western adventure. Value: $3.00-$5.00

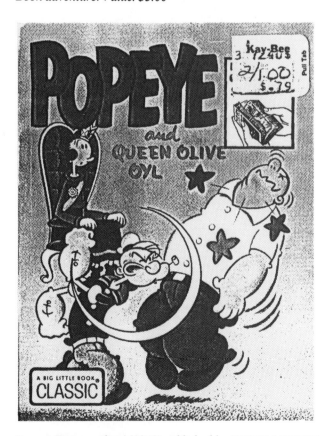

Popeye-Danger Ahoy! (1969) published by WHITMAN PUBLISHING CO. Story by Paul S. Newman. A Big Little Book adventure where The Sea Hag teams up with a Brutus-looking pirate named "Larder" while Popeye and the gang take a movie-making cruise. Value: $5.00-$7.00

PROPHETIC ALLEGORY

POPEYE and the American Dream

Two Classics by E.C. Segar

Introduced & Annotated by

ALAN GOWANS

Popeye and The American Dream (1983) published by AMERICAN LIFE BOOKS. A prophetic allegory of two classic E.C. Segar "Thimble Theatre" comic strips; "The Pool of Youth" and "Popeye's Ark". Value: $5.00-$10.00

Popeye the Sailor (1981) published by TOM DOHERTY ASSOCIATES. Reprinting 1966-67 Popeye comic book stories. Value: $2.00-$4.00

Popeye and The Royal Rat (1981) published by TOM DOHERTY ASSOCIATES. Reprinting 1966-67 Popeye comic book stories. Value: $2.00-$4.00

Popeye the Sailor On Spook Island (1981) published by TOM DOHERTY ASSOCIATES. Reprinting 1966-67 Popeye comic book stories. Value: $2.00-$4.00

THIMBLE THEATRE STARRING POPEYE (1979) published by CHARTER BOOKS. One in a series of paperbacks reprinting Popeye comic strip adventures. This volume features tales from 1961 including the introduction of Popeye's Granny. Stories by Bud Sagendorf. Value: $2.00

MONDO POPEYE (1989) published by ST. MARTINS PRESS. A paperback book reprinting the 1986-88 daily Popeye comic strip stories by Bobby London. Value: $5.95

POPEYE-The Denizen of the Deep (1959) published by L. MILLER & CO. (HACKNEY LTD). This is a comic book published in London reprinting 1954 Popeye comic strip adventures by Tom Sims and Bill Zaboly. Value: $15.00-$20.00

CAP'TAIN PRESENTE; POPEYE (1976) published by LAR. A Popeye comic book from France featuring a mixture of American material and French stories. Value: $5.00

Popeye (first printing 1955) by WONDER BOOKS. Illustrated by Bud Sagendorf. Popeye rescues Wimpy and Swee'pea who get lost at sea. Value varies depending upon which printing you own.

Popeye Goes On A Picnic (first printing in 1958) by WONDER BOOKS. Illustrated by Bud Sagendorf/story by Crosby Newell. Popeye, Olive, Wimpy and Swee'pea share an adventure with a huge whale! Value varies depending upon which printing you own.

Popeye Goes Fishing (1980) by WONDER BOOKS. By Charles Spain Verral. Popeye and Swee'pea do battle with a swordfish while fishing! Value: $1.00

Popeye Climbs A Mountain (1980) by WONDER BOOKS. By Charles Spain Verral. Popeye, Olive and Wimpy climb a mountain top. Value: $1.00

Popeye and The Haunted House (1980) by WONDER BOOKS. By Charles Spain Verral. Popeye, Olive and Swee'pea visit a haunted house . . . which actually is haunted by Bluto! Value: $1.00

Per Un Pugno Di Spinaci (1975) published by OSCAR MONDADORI. An Italian publication reprinting "Thimble Theatre" comic strips from 1939-40 by Tom Sims, Doc Winner and Bela Zaboly. Value Unknown

Diavoli E. Spinaci (1968) published by OSCAR MONDA-DORI. An Italian publication reprinting "Thimble Theatre" comic strips from 1938 by E.C. Segar, Tom Sims and Doc Winner. This book featured an introduction written in English. Value Unknown

Braccio Di Ferro (1976) published by USPI. No. 7. Value Unknown

Braccio Di Ferro (1976) published by USPI. No. 41. Value Unknown

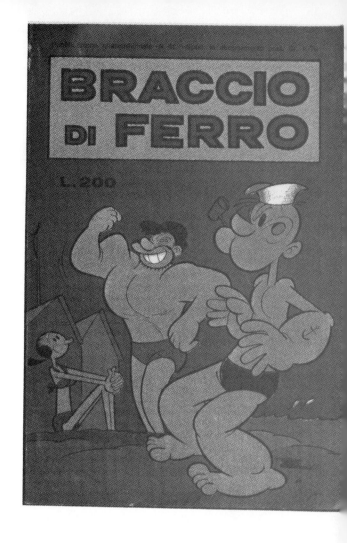

Braccio Di Ferro (1978) published by USPI. No. 48. Value Unknown

Braccio Di Ferro (1978) published by USPI. No. 50. Value Unknown

Braccio Di Ferro (1978) published by USPI. No. 51. Value Unknown

Braccio Di Ferro (1978) published by USPI. No. 52. Value Unknown

Braccio Di Ferro (1978) published by USPI. No. 53. Value Unknown

Braccio Di Ferro (1978) published by USPI. No. 54. Value Unknown

GIVE-A-SHOW PROJECTOR

There is one special collectible from my childhood that brings back pleasant memories and while Popeye was a major part of the product this was not strictly a Popeye toy. During the 1960's, Popeye slides were featured as part of Kenner Toy's "Give-A-Show Projector". This was a plastic, battery-operated projector which you could push cartoon character slides through and project colorful images on the wall. Popeye was but one of the cartoon character slides featured. Other characters included, "Mr. Magoo", "Dick Tracy,", "Rocky and His Friends", "Yogi Bear", "The Flintstones", "Huckleberry Hound", "Bozo the Clown" and several others. In fact you could tell which cartoon characters were popular at various times during the 1960's because of their appearance with this product.

The projector was sold in a big box with cartoon character faces all around the package. The center of the box featured an illustration of a boy and girl shining one of the slides on a wall. The slide which was seen shined on the wall featured a larger illustration of a popular cartoon character. I have seen at least three different boxes where Popeye and both Popeye and Olive together were pictured as the larger illustration. The slides to the projector were also sold individually in small boxes. I recall my parents finding these smaller boxes and reading the front to see which ones featured Popeye, taking all of the Popeye slides out of the different boxes and putting them all in one box. What a surprise I received Christmas morning discovering all Popeye slides in one box when the front listed other slides.

The artwork on each Popeye slide, as well as the other cartoon character slides, was excellent. The artists who worked for Kenner Toys managed to capture the style of each cartoon character beautifully. Though other cartoon characters and superheroes were later added to the sets, Popeye was a mainstay on the product until the entire slide line up was revamped in the early 1970's.

Today "Give-A-Show Projector" is valued between $30.00-$75.00 while the slide boxes are sold between $5.00-$20.00. Whenever I pass a dealer's table and see this toy staring back at me, I recall fond memories from my childhood and isn't that what toy collecting is all about?

Pictured an advertisement which appeared in a children's magazine promoting "Give-A-Show Projector" with Popeye in the spotlight.

Pictured is the box cover to the Kenner's "Give-A-Show Projector" slide shows. Though Popeye is not one of the slides featured in this box, his face, along with Olive Oyl, is spotlighted. Note that Popeye's face (holding a can of spinach) is also used on the box pictured at the far right.

MISCELLANEOUS COLLECTIBLES

In this section are various Popeye pieces including board games, color-by-number sets, banks and colorform sets. Popeye's changing visual design is one of the reasons which makes collecting Popeye material so interesting. The box cover to a color-by-numbers set from the late 1950's will picture the comic strip version of Popeye wearing his Captain's hat while a 1960's set pictures the white uniformed spinach-eater. A 1970's edition will have illustrated the comic strip design, but wearing a sailor's hat. Each color-by-numbers set reflects Popeye's visual appearance of the period. This is also true of Olive Oyl, Swee'pea, Bluto/Brutus and The Sea Hag. Many collectibles will illustrate how the characters are presented during different periods of time.

Popeye Magic Eyes Story Set by SAWYERS/TRU-VUE (1959/1962) This was an early version of the viewmaster toy. Slides which were featured in this collectible have later appeared as viewmaster packs. Artwork on the slides was done by Popeye comic strip artists, Bill Zaboly and Bud Sagendorf. Value: $12.00-$25.00

Popeye Getar by MATTEL INC. (1951/1953) A children's guitar in the shape of Popeye's face a child could crank and play "I'm Popeye the Sailor Man". The pipe was removable so you could pretend to strum the guitar's strings. Value: $45.00-$65.00

Front & back box designs for MATTEL'S Popeye Getar.

Popeye Magic Play Around by AMSO (late 1950's). This was a play set which could be assembled. There were Popeye character figures, each with a magnetic base. A child could use a magent to slide the characters across the play set. A nicely detailed Popeye piece. Value: $45.00

Popeye Crazy Color Foam by AMERICAN AEROSOL CORPORATION (1980). When you squeeze the back of the can, white crazy foam squirts out of Popeye's mouth. Value: $3.00-$5.00

Popeye Bubble Liquid by M. SHIMMEL SONS INC. (1970's). A bubble liquid container in the shape of Popeye. Popeye's facial design is based on the King Features TV-cartoons and note that he's wearing a necktie similar to his sailor's knot. Value: $5.00

Popeye Music Box manufacturer unknown (1980). A colorful music box and when you opened the drawer, "I'm Popeye the Sailor Man" music would play and the Popeye figure in the center would dance a little jig. Value: $25.00

S.S. Popeye wallets (1960's) manufacturer unknown. Wallets featuring a Popeye drawing which moves as you move the front of the wallet. Value: $20.00

Popeye Wallet manufacturer unknown but probably LARAMI (1978) Value: $1.00-$2.00. A small brown wallet with the comic strip version of Popeye illustrated on the front.

Popeye Gumball Machine by HASBRO (1968) A gumball machine in the shape of Popeye's head. The original version of this toy featured Popeye's head unpainted so that a child could see the gumballs. I remember going crazy when I received this for my birthday in 1970. Value: $10.00

Popeye Head Bank by PLAY-PAL PLASTICS (1972). A plastic head of Popeye which could be used as a bank. Value: $5.00-$7.00

Popeye Plastic Bank by RENZ CORP. (1976). A plastic bank in the shape of Popeye's head. The "Popeye" logo is indented in the sailor's Captain's hat. Value: $8.00-$10.00

Popeye Money Bank by BBI TOYS INTERNATIONAL (1986) A Plastic bank (with removable pipe) in the shape of Popeye's head. Value: $3.00

Popeye Carrying Holder by RENZ CORP. (1979). A holder for candy or small objects with a "Trick or Treat" tag attached to it. Value: $5.00

A Popeye bank my mother made for me in a ceramic class. This is the basic mold for Popeye's head used in making an object of this kind.

Popeye Spinach Can by MATTEL (1957). A spinach can with a figure of Popeye's head which can be shoved back inside the can. The can is marked "Popeye Spinach". The side of the can pictures Olive feeling Popeye's muscle while Popeye says, "I Yam what I Yam cause I eats me Spinach. Spinach is Good for me muskles." On the back features an illustration of Wimpy giving a recipe for Spinach Burgers; "To one can of spinach . . . add sliced roll . . . remove can, heat and eat." Value: $45.00

Popeye Toothbrush set by NASTA (1980's) Popeye is in a boat which is actually a toothbrush dispenser. Value: $5.00

Popeye Color and Re-Color Book by JACK BUILT (1957). Art inside was based on the comic strip Popeye version and illustration by Bill Zaboly/written by Tom Sims. The set came with a box of crayons attached to the right hand corner of the cover, which my dog began to eat when I put this book down one Christmas morning. Value: $20.00-$25.00

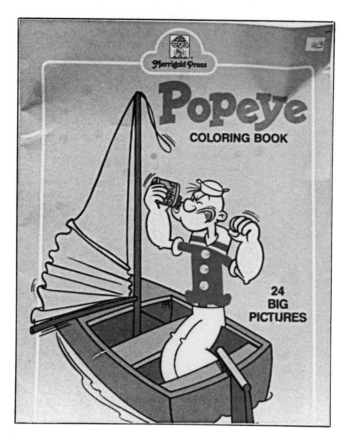

Popeye Coloring Book by MERRIGOLD PRESS (1981). An oversized Popeye coloring book based on the comic strip versions of the Popeye cast. Value: $2.00

Popeye head Silly Puddy Containers (1950's/1960's) manufacturer unknown. Art on Popeye's head by Bill Zaboly. Value: $5.00-$7.00 each

Popeye Pop-Up Book by PETER HADDOCK LIMITED "Popeye Goes Gardening" (1987). Value: $2.00

Popeye Pop-Up Book by PETER HADDOCK LIMITED "Popeye's Surprise Present" (1987). Value: $2.00

Popeye Pop-Up Book by PETER HADDOCK LIMITED "Popeye and The Pet" (1987). Value: $2.00

Popeye Pop-Up Book by PETER HADDOCK LIMITED "Popeye Goes Fishing" (1987). Value: $2.00

The back of a Popeye Pop-Up Book advertising the other Popeye books in this series produced in London. Swee'pea was drawn without his nose!?!

Popeye's Spinach Truck by MATCHBOX (1980) A figure of Popeye in a truck with a barrel marked "Popeye's Spinach". Value: $5.00

Olive Oyl Car by MATCHBOX (1980). A figure of Olive Oyl in a sportscar! Value: $5.00

Bluto in a Steamroller by MATCHBOX (1980). A figure of Bluto driving a steamroller. Value: $5.00

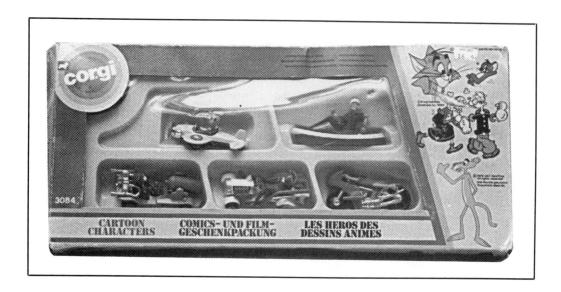

Corgi Cartoon Characters (1979). A boxed set featuring cartoon characters in cars. This set included, Tom & Jerry, The Pink Panther, Olive Oyl in an airplane and Popeye in a sailboat. This is a French edition of the toy. Value: $6.95 (Courtesy of Steve Higgins)

Popeye Patch (1970's) manufacturer unknown. One in a series of Popeye character patches. Popeye appears in his white sailor's uniform from the 1960-61 King Features TV cartoons. Value: $5.00-$7.00

Popeye Lite-Brite by HASBRO (1978). A Popeye picture refill set for the Lite-Brite toy. The picture of Popeye on the package is how the sailor appeared in Hanna Barbera's "All New Popeye Hour" cartoons (1978-83). Value: $7.00

Popeye and Swee'pea Mirror by CREATIVE ACCESSORIES (late 1980's). Value: $48.00

Popeye Sticker Fun-Pre-School Activity by LOWE (1960's). A Popeye cut-out figure with Popeye sticker activities. A small pair of scissors was included. Value: $20.00

Popeye Sun Cards by TILLMAN'S (1962). Box is labeled "Sun-eze" and features three negative-style pictures of King Features TV version of Popeye, Olive Oyl and Wimpy. By exposing negatives to sunlight you could print your pictures. Popeye is featured in his white sailor's collar on the front of the box. He also has white around the black pupil of his eye; a characteristic of the animated Popeye! Value: $6.00-$8.00

Popeye and Olive Phone Rests by COMVU CORPORATION (1980's). Value: $3.00-$5.00

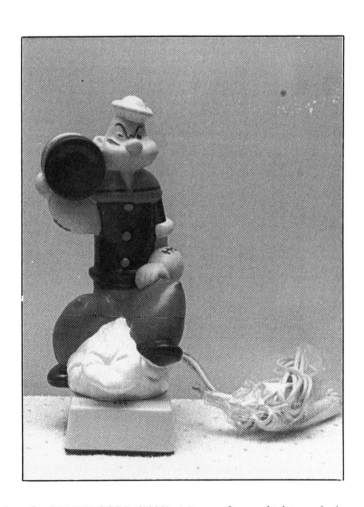

Popeye Telephone by COMVU CORP. (1982). A Popeye figure which is a telephone. Value: $20.00

FASSON Popeye Stickers (1981) - all featuring the comic strip version of the Popeye cast. Value: 69¢

Popeye Blow Bubble Pipe manufacturer unknown (1969). Popeye's collar is based on the white sailor suit design from the Famous Studios/King Features TV cartoons. Value: $7.00-$10.00

Popeye & Pal Bookmarks by DURHAM INDUSTRIES (1980): Popeye. Value: $2.00

Popeye & Pal Bookmarks by DURHAM INDUSTRIES (1980): Olive Oyl. Value: $2.00

Popeye & Pal Bookmarks by DURHAM INDUSTRIES (1980): Brutus (the comic strip version). Value: $2.00

Popeye Spinach Can by GARDNER (late 1950's). These cans were part of a Popeye target game featuring illustrations of Popeye and Bluto having a tug of war over a bowl of spinach. The can is marked "Popeye Spinach-100 Points". Value: $5.00 per can

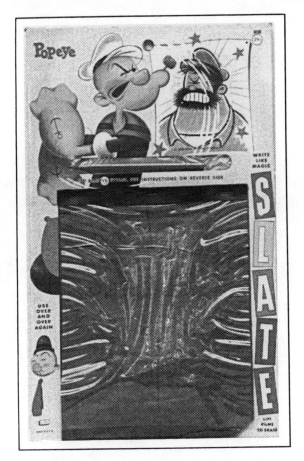

Popeye Magic Slate by LOWE (1960). The comic strip version of Popeye is seen punching the Fleischer version/comic strip design of Bluto. Value: $20.00

Popeye Magic Slate by LOWE (1963). Pictured on the slate are the King Features TV-versions of Popeye (seen in white sailor's suit), Olive Oyl, Wimpy and Brutus. Value: $20.00

Popeye Trash Can, manufacturer unknown. This collectible has an interesting purchasing background surrounding it. I had called a dealer and asked if he had any 1950's Popeye material. He informed me he had a Popeye trash can from the 1950's with Popeye, Olive and Brutus pictured on it. He not only said it was from the 1950's but advertised it in a trade publication as being from this period. I was very excited when I heard of the can and had visions of 1950's or Famous Studios style art work on it. I gave the dealer his $50.00 asking price and was shocked and dismayed to discover the can featured artwork which was drawn for the 1979 publication "Popeye-The First Fifty Years". The can was actually a piece from the early 1980's and the dealer dated this collectible without doing any research and pulled "1950's" out of the clear blue sky! There was no copyright date on the can. Please learn from my mistake and before purchasing any collectible whether on Popeye or any other cartoon/comic strip character...ask questions! I'm keeping this can in my collection to remind myself to do just that. Value: $5.00

Well...not a Popeye collectible...but a clay head of the sailor I made in Junior High School.

Popeye View master Packet by VIEW-MASTER (1962). This packet contained 3 Popeye adventures "Paint Ahoy", "Popeye's Missile Muscle" & "Swee'pea's Edjamacation". Art work on slides by Bud Sagendorf.

The pages from the View-Master booklet which was sold with the Popeye View Master slides: (1962).

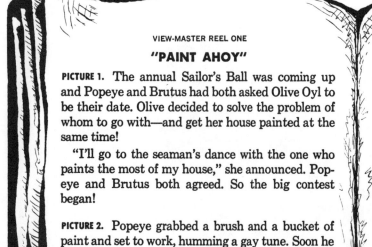

VIEW-MASTER REEL ONE

"PAINT AHOY"

PICTURE 1. The annual Sailor's Ball was coming up and Popeye and Brutus had both asked Olive Oyl to be their date. Olive decided to solve the problem of whom to go with—and get her house painted at the same time!

"I'll go to the seaman's dance with the one who paints the most of my house," she announced. Popeye and Brutus both agreed. So the big contest began!

PICTURE 2. Popeye grabbed a brush and a bucket of paint and set to work, humming a gay tune. Soon he was far ahead of the boastful but lazy Brutus. Seeing his chance for a date with Olive slipping away, Brutus decided that if he couldn't paint faster than Popeye, then he'd have to come up with a scheme for slowing his rival down.

And if there was one thing that Brutus was good at, it was thinking up evil schemes! He moved his ladder just around the corner from Popeye, climbed up with his paint bucket and . . .

PICTURE 3. KER-SPLASH! Brutus tipped his paint bucket, accidently-on-purpose, right on Popeye's head!

"YIKE!" gulped Popeye. Spitting and sputtering, he tumbled from the ladder, covered from head to toe with sticky red paint!

PICTURE. 4. "Swee'pea!" bellowed Popeye, "I yam blinded with this stuff! Bring me some turpentine, —quick!"

Swee'pea came bouncing to Popeye's aid with turpentine, rags, and bowl, and they set about cleaning up the mess that Brutus had caused. As Popeye rubbed and scrubbed and brushed and wiped, Brutus, snickering an evil snicker, was painting away at Olive's house and quickly went ahead in the contest.

"Hurry up, Popeye," Swee'pea warned, for he wanted Popeye to win.

PICTURE 5. Seeing how far ahead Brutus was, Popeye knew that it was time for him to produce his secret weapon—SPINACH!

Whipping out a big can, Popeye downed it at a gulp.

NOW I'LL CATCH UP!

"Don't worry, Swee'pea! I'll catch up!" he said. "With me spinach makin' me muskles bigger an' me super brain at work, Brutus won't have a chance!"

"Wheeee!" shouted Swee'pea, for he knew that when Popeye had his spinach, there was always plenty of action coming up.

PICTURE 6. Again grabbing his brush and paint bucket, Popeye was off like a jet! Starting at the very tip of the roof, he raced 'round and 'round the house,

painting everything in sight with one continuous stroke. The startled Brutus could only stand there gawking with astonishment at the flying sailor!

" 'Round and 'round I goes," laughed Popeye, "and where I stops—nobody knows!" And when Brutus got in the way of his flying brush, Popeye just painted him, too!

PICTURE 7. So Popeye was the winner!

"Oh, Popeye! You were wonderful!" cooed Olive Oyl, even though Popeye's speedy paint job had included the house roof and even covered all the windows!

"Aw, it was nothin'," said Popeye modestly, giving all the credit to the spinach.

And happy little Swee'pea just laughed and laughed at the sight of big Brutus, who was still trying to figure out what had hit him!

VIEW-MASTER REEL TWO

"MISSILE MUSCLE"

PICTURE 1. "Attention! Attention!" the radio screamed. The frantic announcer had terrifying news; a huge rocket had been fired accidentally and was whooshing around the sky out of control!

"Hide! Duck! Run!" he shouted, "Don't stand there, DO SOMETHING!"

And Olive Oyl knew just what to do. She screamed, "YIKE!?!" jumped three feet into the air, ran around the room five times, and then raced out of the door screeching, "Popeye! POP-EYE!"

HELP!

PICTURE 2. "HELP, POP-EYE! SAVE US!!!"

Popeye heard Olive Oyl's cries and came running outside. Seeing the huge rocket spurting crazily around the sky, he quickly decided that, "This is a job for SPINACH!"

Out came the can, off went the lid, and down the hatch went a mighty gulp of the powerful vegetable. Popeye's muscles trembled, his whole body stiffened as the spinach took effect. He turned his pipe upside down and flames began to shoot from the bowl.

"Ten," he said, "nine, eight, seven, six . . ."

PICTURE 3. "BLAST OFF," he shouted. "Here I goes, I yam an anti-missile missile!"

His little pipe spurting flame, Popeye shot higher and higher into the sky, his spinach-powered fist poised to slug it out with the mighty rocket!

PICTURE. 4. But the rocket wouldn't fight! It dodged

and twisted and turned through the clouds, almost as though it were afraid of Popeye!

Maneuvering his pipe skillfully, Popeye took up the chase. Up and down and around they went as Popeye tried frantically to head it off before it crashed.

Down below, Olive trembled and twittered, "Oh, save me, Popeye, save me!"

PICTURE 5. With a final twist of his pipe, Popeye caught the rocket head-on! Right at each other the missile and the man sped . . . one of them charged with a mighty atomic warhead, the other with spinach.

It would be the collision of the century—could Popeye possibly survive the atomic blast? Could the missile endure Popeye's powerful punch?

PICTURE 6. KA-BOWPOWCRASHBANGBLOOIE!!!

The mighty roar from the meeting of the two speeding forces echoed across the countryside. The clouds were blasted from the sky by the explosion, the trees were stripped of their leaves, the earth shook . . . even Olive Oyl trembled.

Out of the mushroom cloud caused by the blast came hurtling fragments of rocket—and a bedraggled, blackened figure of Popeye. Could he have possibly survived?

PICTURE 7. As his battered body plowed into the ground, Olive ran up, patting her hair in place.

Ignoring her boyfriend's condition, she gushed, "Popeye, you're wonderful! I haven't a scratch on me!" At this, the figure on the ground stirred, and one eye quivered and opened slightly.

"HUH?" Popeye croaked. "I yam glad to hear you ain't mussed up none, Olive. Do ya think ya could gets me another can o' spinach to revive ME some?"

VIEW-MASTER REEL THREE

"SWEE'PEAS EDJAMACATION"

PICTURE 1. "Well, Blow Me Down!" said Popeye, and Olive Oyl just about did.

"You should be ashamed of yourself! You're a horrible beast!" she screamed.

All Popeye had done was to insist that Swee'pea had to start to school. But the nearest school was two miles away, and there was no school bus. Olive said that Popeye was cruel and heartless to even THINK of sending a little boy that far to school—and, of course, Swee'pea agreed.

PICTURE 2. Even Wimpy agreed—between hamburgers—that it was too far for Swee'pea to travel. Popeye grumbled, as older folks often do, about how much harder he'd had it when he was going to school, but that didn't solve the problem.

He was clearly outvoted; Swee'pea couldn't walk to school. So how was he going to get there?

PICTURE 3. While Popeye puzzled over the problem, Swee'pea decided to put in his two cents worth. "Maybe if I screams loud enough," he thought, "Popeye will get tired of hearing all the fuss and say I don't have to go after all."

"WA-A-A-A!!" he cried, "If you loved your little boy kid you'd do something about the school!"

Popeye yelled, "Do something about the school, ya say, Swee'pea? Ya gives me an idea!"

PICTURE. 4. Popeye whipped out a big can of spinach (he always kept some on hand for just such emergencies) and downed it with a gulp and a slurp and a smack of his lips.

"Now," he said, "I yam off to do something about that schoolhouse for ya, Swee'pea."

Swee'pea jumped up and down with excitement. He didn't know what Popeye was up to, but he did know that spinach always meant action.

PICTURE 5. Popeye galloped off down the road. Six minutes and two miles later he stopped before the schoolhouse where a class was in session. Popeye politely knocked on the door.

"Excuse me, Ma'am," he said to the teacher, "but my little boy kid Swee'pea needs an edjama-

cation so's he can talk good like his Daddy—me! It's too far for him to walk so I'd like to borry the schoolhouse if you don't mind."

"Borrow the schoolhouse?" asked the teacher.

"Yes'm," said Popeye. "You just tell all the little boy and girl kids to batten their hatches and I'll give 'em a geogerfy lesson!"

PICTURE 6. With that Popeye scooped up the schoolhouse, astounded teacher, students and all, and

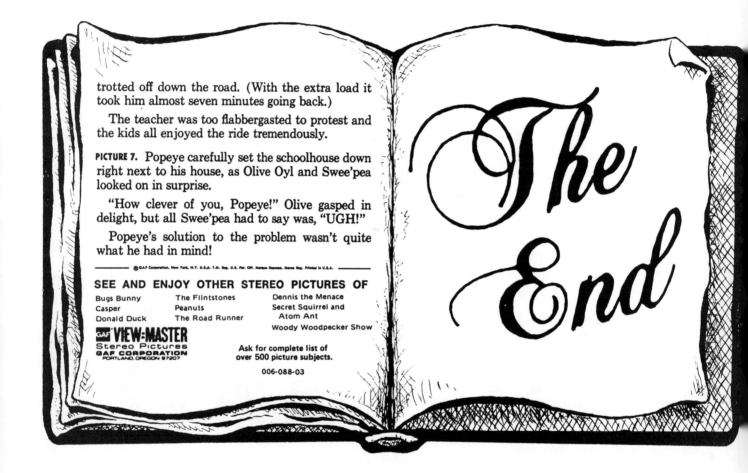

trotted off down the road. (With the extra load it took him almost seven minutes going back.)

The teacher was too flabbergasted to protest and the kids all enjoyed the ride tremendously.

PICTURE 7. Popeye carefully set the schoolhouse down right next to his house, as Olive Oyl and Swee'pea looked on in surprise.

"How clever of you, Popeye!" Olive gasped in delight, but all Swee'pea had to say was, "UGH!"

Popeye's solution to the problem wasn't quite what he had in mind!

©GAF Corporation, New York, N.Y. U.S.A. T.M. Reg. U.S. Pat. Off. Marque Deposee. Marca Reg. Printed in U.S.A.

SEE AND ENJOY OTHER STEREO PICTURES OF

Bugs Bunny   The Flintstones   Dennis the Menace
Casper   Peanuts   Secret Squirrel and
Donald Duck   The Road Runner   Atom Ant
                                            Woody Woodpecker Show

GAF VIEW-MASTER
Stereo Pictures
GAF CORPORATION
PORTLAND, OREGON 97207

Ask for complete list of
over 500 picture subjects.

006-088-03

The End

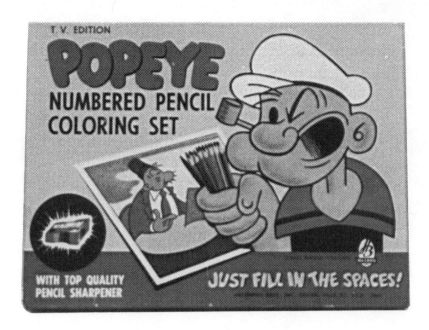

POPEYE NUMBERED PENCIL & COLORING SET by HASSENFELD BROS. (1957) An early Popeye pencil by numbers set featuring the comic strip character designs. Value: $30.00-$45.00

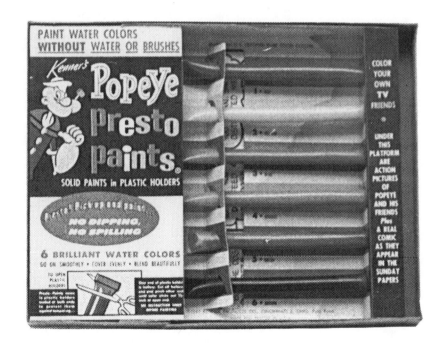

Popeye Presto Paints by KENNER (1961). You could apply water color style paints to the pictures in this set. The pictures were drawn by Bill Zaboly and Bud Sagendorf. The cover stated, "Color your own comics and TV favorites as they appear in the Sunday papers". By billing Popeye in this manner, Kenner mentions not only his popularity as a comic strip character but as a TV favorite as well. Value: $35.00

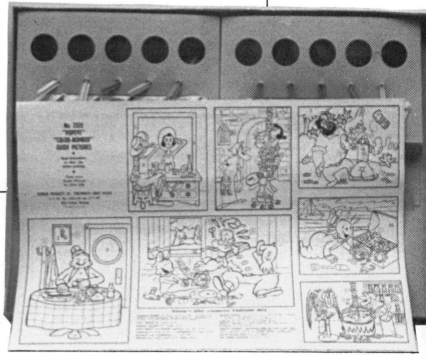

Popeye's Sparkle Paints by KENNER PRODUCTS (1966) This set contained pictures of both the King Features TV cartoon version & comic strip designs of the Popeye cast. One of the rare pieces to include the King Features TV cartoon version of the Sea Hag. Along with the pictures were 10 "jewel-like colors". The colors were actually glitter paints used to color in the pictures. Note that the King Features TV version of Olive Oyl is holding on to a comic strip designed picture of Popeye on a rocket. Value: $12.00-$20.00

HASBRO Popeye Paint and Crayon Set (1960's). The pictures in the set were the comic strips versions of the Popeye cast while the King Features TV cartoon versions of Popeye and Swee'Pea appeared on the cover. Value: $20.00

Popeye Paint and Crayon Set by HASBRO (1970's). Since the 1950's, Hasbro has been producing Popeye Paint & Crayon sets. Usually each set has contained the same pictures to color but with different box cover illustrations. The drawings of Swee'Pea, Wimpy, Olive and Popeye are all based on the comic strip designs of the characters. Value: $7.00-$10.00

POPEYE

WIMPY

OLIVE OYL

The artwork which appeared in the POPEYE PRESTO PAINT SET by Kenner Toys illustrated by Bill Zaboly with the Olive Oyl drawing by Bud Sagendorf.

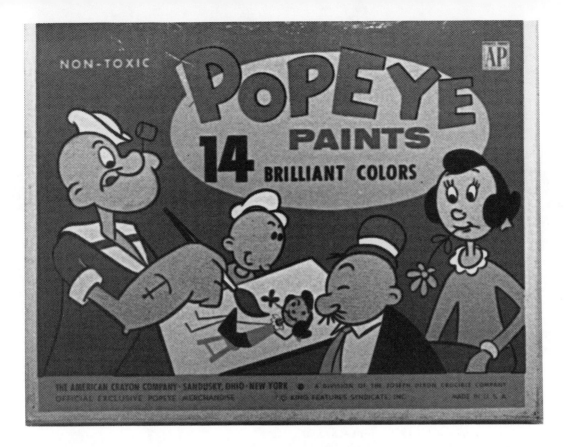

Popeye Paints-14 Brilliant Colors by the AMERICAN CRAYON CO. (1965). Don't let the lines on Popeye's collar fool you, the illustrations of Popeye, Swee'pea, Wimpy and Olive are all based on the 1960-61 King Features TV cartoons. Value: $25.00

Give-A-Show Projector by KENNER (1960). One of the first Give-A-Show Projector sets featuring Popeye as the headliner. The illustration of Popeye was drawn by Bill Zaboly. Value: $45.00

Give-A-Show Projector by KENNER (1964). During the mid-1960's Popeye was still billed as the main attraction and was featured with different slides until the cartoon character line-up was revamped in the 1970's. Value: $35.00

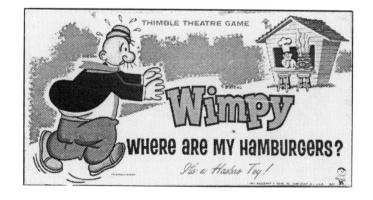

Thimble Theatre Game starring Wimpy by HASBRO (1965). This was a board game starring Wimpy in "Where are my Hamburgers?" Wimpy had to follow a trail to reach a hamburger stand. Lil' Swee'pea was pictured on the game's board but Popeye was no where to be found! Value: $30.00

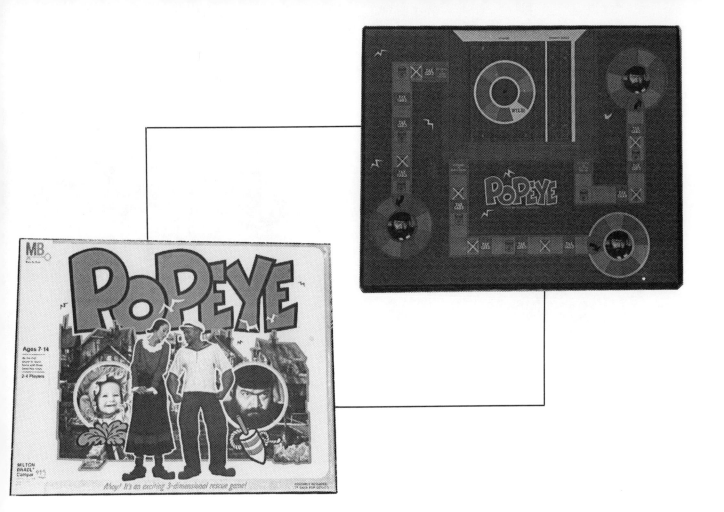

Popeye Board Game by MILTON BRADLEY (1980). This 3-dimensional rescue game was based on the Popeye live-action feature film starring Robin Williams. The Popeye movie was actually based on Segar "Thimble Theatre" strips from the 1930's. Value: $5.00

Popeye Board Game by PARKER BROTHERS (1983). A board game which was based on the popular Popeye arcade game featuring the King Features TV cartoon designs of Popeye, Olive, The Sea Hag and Brutus. Value: $5.00

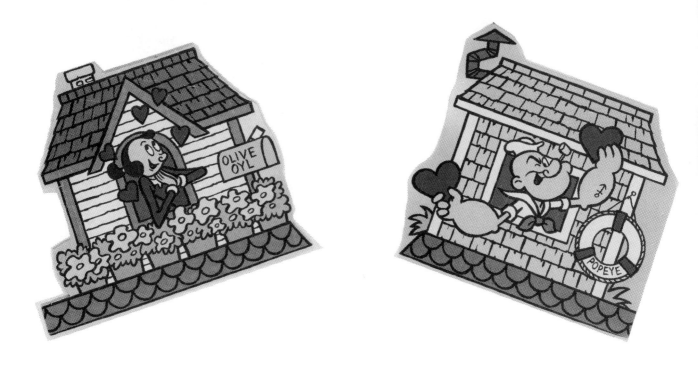

Illustrations of Popeye and Olive Oyl as they appeared on the 1983 Parker Brothers Board Game. Their visual designs are based on the 1960-61 King Features TV cartoons.

Popeye Cartoon Kit by COLORFORMS (1957). One of the first colorform sets introduced and the first to feature Popeye. While the comic strip version of Popeye and Olive are illustrated on the front of the box, the Famous Studios designs of Popeye, Olive and Bluto are featured inside. This was a collectible based on the success the Popeye threatre cartoons were having on television. This is also one of the few collectibles featuring Bluto in his white Navy uniform. Colorforms are usually hard to locate at dealer's tables, but, I often see this set (or a larger sized version) turn up often. Value depends upon which size you get: $45.00-$50.00

The instruction booklet to the 1957 POPEYE CARTOON KIT featuring the Famous Studios designs for Popeye, Olive and Bluto.

Popeye the Weatherman by COLORFORMS (1959). Popeye helps his lil' pal how to dress for various kinds of weather. Billed as "Official Popeye Weatherman Kit made only by Colorforms". The figures of Popeye and his lil' pal look as though they were doll-constructed and photographed for the set. Value: $20.00

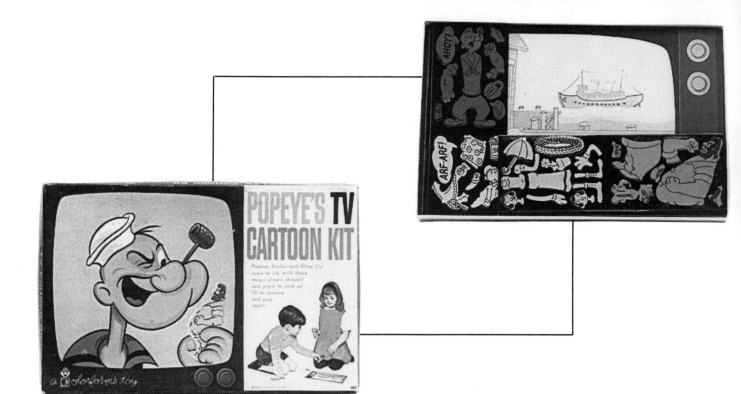

Popeye's TV Cartoon Kit by COLORFORMS (1966). Though the comic strip version of Popeye is pictured on the front of the box, the sailor is pictured holding the King Features TV-cartoon design of Brutus. The actual colorform pieces in this set were based on the King Features TV cartoon versions of Olive Oyl, Brutus, Swee'pea and a white-suited designed Popeye. Note how the set is billed as a "TV Cartoon Kit". The board you placed the colorform shapes on was illustrated like a television set...complete with dials! Value: $20.00

Popeye Cartoon Set by COLORFORMS (1970's). The colorform pieces are based on the comic strip designs featuring Popeye, Olive, Wimpy, The Jeep, Swee'pea and Brutus! Value: $10.00

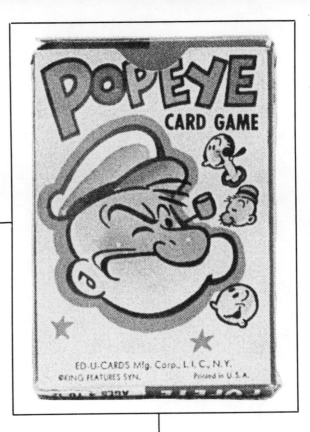

Directions for Playing
"POPEYE"
CARD GAME

The rules for this game are similar to "Rummy". First shuffle the cards thoroughly and deal out one at a time, face down, until each player has 6 cards (7 cards if 2 play). Place the remaining cards in a pile, face down, on the table. Take top card and turn face up next to the "drawing pile". This starts the "discard pile".

Player to the left of dealer begins game by taking the top card from either the drawing or discard pile and can then lay down matching cards if he has 3 or more alike or 3 or more cards with consecutive numbers in each series . . . such as No. 1, 2, 3, "SPINACH" cards or 7, 8, 9, 10 "ANCHOR" cards, etc. When he can make no more plays he must discard one card by placing it face up on the discard pile. Then the next player to his left goes and the play continues in the same way around the table.

Any player in his turn may place cards on his own or other players' "layouts" that will complete matching sets or can add to either end of a series **provided he can go out when so doing. In** this case he may discard one last card if necessary.

The first one to clear his hand of all cards is the winner and receives the total number of points remaining in his opponents hands. If all cards in the drawing pile are used up before there is a winner the discard pile may be shuffled and turned face down to form a new drawing pile.

Ed-U-Cards Mfg. Corp., L.I.C., New York

Popeye Card Game (1960's) by ED-U-CARDS Value: $10.00-$15.00

The cards that appeared in the Popeye ED-U-CARD package.

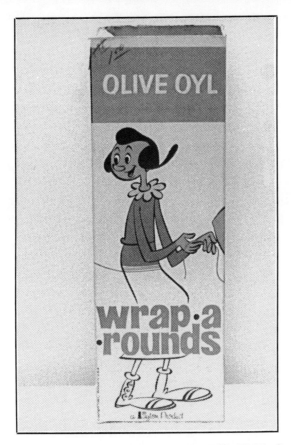

Popeye Wrap-A-Round Playmates by PAYTON PRODUCTS (1961). Set contained cutouts you could link together with yarn or use as stand up figures. The characters were billed as "4-Popeye Television Character Action Figures". Pictured is the Olive Oyl illustration, based on the 1960-61 King Features TV version, on the box. Value: $20.00

Popeye illustration, based on the comic strip design, seen on the box of PAYTON PRODUCTS Popeye Wrap-a-Round Playmates.

Wimpy illustration seen on the box of PAYTON PRODUCTS Popeye Wrap-a-Round Play-mates.

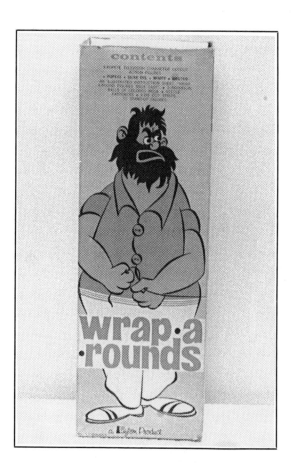

Brutus illustration, based on the King Features TV-cartoon design, seen on the box of PAY-TON PRODUCTS Popeye Wrap-a-Round Playmates.

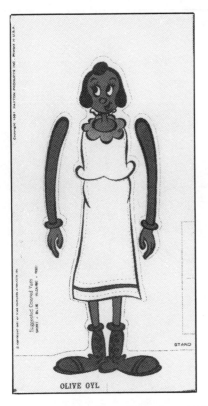 

The Olive Oyl cut-out figure from PAYTON PRODUCTS Popeye Wrap-a-Round Playmates. The character design of Olive is based on the 1960-61 King Features TV-cartoon version.

The Popeye cut-out figure from PAYTON PRODUCTS Popeye Wrap-a-Round Playmates. The character design for the sailor is based on the 1960-61 King Features TV-cartoons. Note that Popeye is illustrated in his white sailor's suit despite the fact he's seen wearing his comic strip costume on this product's box.

The Wimpy cut-out figure from PAYTON PRODUCTS Popeye Wrap-a-Round Playmates.

The Brutus cut-out figure from PAYTON PRODUCTS Popeye Wrap-a-Round Playmates. Brutus' visual design is based on how he appeared in the 1960-61 King Features TV-cartoons.

Popeye Interlocking Picture Puzzle by JAYMAR (1950's/1960's). This 100 piece puzzle was titled, "Three's a Crowd" and featured Brutus paying a call on Olive Oyl. Value: $10.00

Popeye Inlaid Puzzle by JAYMAR (1950's-1960's). This was a TV-tray style puzzle featuring Popeye's battle with a lion! Value: $7.00-$10.00

Popeye 28 piece Kiddie Puzzle by JAYMAR (1980's). This puzzle originally appeared during the 1950's-1960's and is pictured in its repackaged box for the 1980's. Value: $3.00

Popeye & Son Puzzles by MILTON BRADLEY (1988). Milton Bradley produced a series of Popeye puzzles based on the characters from the "Popeye & Son" cartoon series. Value of each puzzle: $2.99

Several companies have produced Popeye T-shirts over the years. Some feature Popeye while others have showcased Olive Oyl, Wimpy or Brutus. Pictured are a few T-shirt designs. The full length pose of Popeye looking at his muscle was taken from a publicity drawing used by the Fleischer Studios during the 1930's.

Pictured are Popeye Post Cards which were sold in Malta during the production of the POPEYE feature film starring Robin Williams. Some postcards featured sets from the movie while others had Popeye drawings pictured. Courtesy of Kevin Ghaffari of PIX POSTER CELLAR in Cambridge, MA.

145

Popeye stickers by DIAMOND TOYMAKERS (1983). Pictured are puffy stickers of Olive Oyl, Popeye, Brutus and The Sea Hag based on their character designs from the 1960-61 King Features TV cartoons. Sold in a set; Value: $3.00

During January of 1989, Popeye had his own special 900 number children could call and hear the sailor's adventures! Kids could also write to Popeye and receive Popeye stickers in honor of Popeye's 60th birthday. Pictured is Larry Harmon's version of Popeye who appeared in several of the King Features TV cartoons. Larry Harmon is better known as the man behind the World's Most Famous Clown, "BOZO".

WILTON Popeye cake pan (1980). You can make a cake in the shape of Popeye's face. Value: $4.00

The flip side to the Popeye cake pan by Wilton.

Popeye tattoo bubble gum by TOPPS CHEWING GUM (1950's/1960's). You could chew the gum and rub tattoos on your skin! Value: $5.00

Popeye Spinach by ALLEN CANNING CO. Still sold in many areas!

Magazine ad promoting ALLEN'S POPEYE SPINACH.

Popeye Candy Box No. 3 by PHOENIX CANDY CO. (1979). Pictured is a scene from Hanna Barbera's "All New Popeye Hour" cartoons. The box was filled with lil' candy and a prize. Value: $5.00

Popeye Candy Box No. 6 by PHOENIX CANDY CO. (1979). Pictured on the box are Bluto and Popeye as they appeared in the "All New Popeye Hour" cartoons produced by Hanna Barbera. Value: $5.00

Popeye shredded bubble gum by AMUROL PRODUCTS (1987). Green colored bubble gum. Still available in many areas.

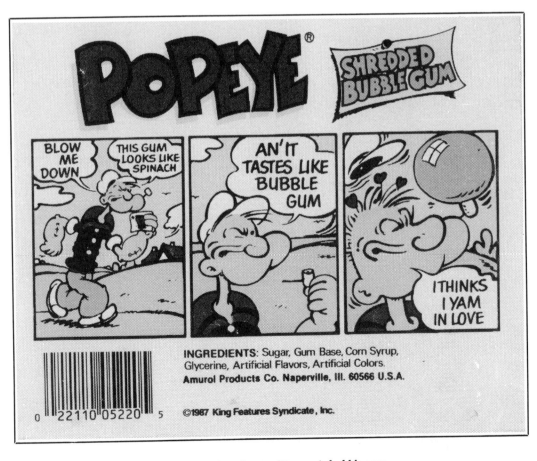

The back illustrated package of Popeye's bubble gum.

The box which POPEYE'S FAMOUS FRIED CHICKEN uses to contain their chicken. The illustration of Popeye is based on the King Feautures TV-cartoons. Note the big pipe and the white around the black pupil of his eye. These eating places have become extremely popular.

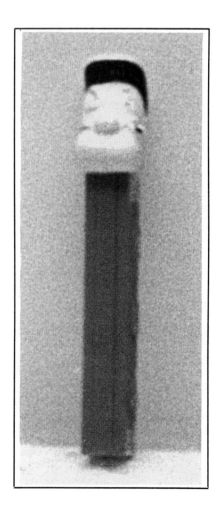

Popeye PEZ Dispenser by PEZ (1950's-early 1960's). The original Popeye PEZ dispenser wearing his Captain's hat. Value: $5.00

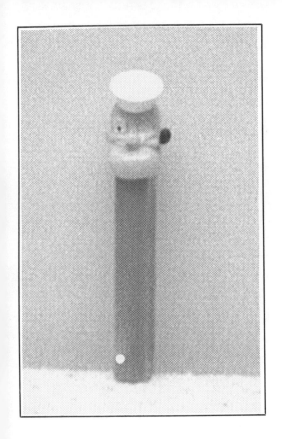

Popeye PEZ Dispenser by PEZ (mid-1960's/1970's) Popeye is wearing his sailor's hat. This Popeye produced along with a Brutus and Olive Oyl PEZ. Value: $25.00-$50.00

Popeye Lunch Box by KING SEELEY THERMOS (1964). This lunch box featured illustrations of the comic strip designs of Popeye, Olive, Wimpy and Swee'pea but the King Features TV-cartoon version of Brutus. Value: $20.00-$25.00

The Thermos to the 1964 Popeye lunch box.

Popeye Lunch Box by ALADDIN INDUSTRIES (1980). This lunch box featured illustrations of the comic strip cast. Illustrations of Alice the Goon, Eugene the Jeep, Rough House, Pappy and Granny were featured around the sides of the box. Value: $3.25-$5.00

The Thermos to the 1980 lunch box.

The Thermos to the Popeye & Son lunch box featuring the "Popeye & Son" logo.

Popeye and Son Plastic Lunchbox by THERMO-SERV (1987). A raised pictured style lunch box based on the "Popeye & Son" cartoon series. Value: $6.00

Brutus Coca-Cola Glass (1977) pictured on the glass is the King Features TV cartoon version of Brutus. Value: $5.00

Olive Oyl Drinking Mug by DEKA (1971) Value: $2.95   *Popeye Cast Drinking Mug by DEKA (1971). Value: $2.95*

Popeye Cereal Bowl by DEKA (1971). A unique bowl as both the King Features TV-cartoon versions and comic strip designs of Popeye, Olive, Wimpy, Swee'pea and Brutus are featured along the bowl. Value: $5.00

Popeye Coca Cola Glass (1975) featuring Popeye in his white sailor's uniform. Value: $7.00

Popeye Drinking Glass by DEKA (1971) The King Features-TV cartoon designs of Popeye, Olive Oyl, Wimpy, Swee'pea and Brutus were illustrated around the glass. Value: $5.00

POPEYE

in

GHOST SHIP TO TREASURE ISLAND

by

Paul S. Newman

Authorized Edition
WHITMAN PUBLISHING COMPANY
Racine, Wisconsin

"I Saw What I Saw!"

A Small Stowaway

The Goon Is Too Late

The Sea Hag!

Popeye Minds the Helm

Popeye's Secret Weapon

A Giant Wave

A Spinach-Powered Blow!

An Overgrown Pretzel!

Olive Is Captured

The Shark Pit!

"Hand Over Your Spinach!"

Popeye Charges

Popeye Reacts

Wild Spinach for Popeye

"I Am Coming!"

Stunned Sharks

Muscles Surrenders

The Sea Hag Again

Popeye pounding the man in black is from "Per Un Pugno Di Spinaci" by Tom Sims, Doc Winner and Bela Zaboly. Published by OSCAR MONDADORI (1975).

Popeye getting stomped on is from the Italian strip reprint book, "Diavoli E. Spinaci" by E.C. Segar, Tom Sims & Doc Winner. Published by OSCAR MONDADORI (1968).

Wimpy's schemes to get hamburgers are understood in any language. The scene in Italian is from "Pisellino Volante" from Braccio Di Ferro No. 48 (1978). The scene in English originally appeared in a 1966 Popeye comic book story titled, "The Great Balloon Fraud" which was later reprinted in the paperback book, "Popeye and The Royal Rat" published by TOM DOHERTY ASSOCIATES.

Popeye (1976) published by USPI. No. 7. Value Unknown

Popeye (1976) published by USPI. No. 8. Value Unk.

Braccio Di Ferro No. 48 featured a "Timoteo" story, "Il Medico Degli Alberi". "Timoteo" is Brutus in Italian. Note how he's wearing a sailor's hat rather than his American counterpart's Captain's hat. Published by USPI (1978).

Pappy Takes the Wheel

"Put It Back!"

Pappy takes the wheel from the 1969 Big Little Book, "Danger Ahoy"!

The Sea Hag joins forces with a Brutus-looking Pirate in "Danger Ahoy"!

Popeye Ducks Quickly

Swee' Pea Helps Out

The Sea Hag is about to get yanked off her feet by a cannon ball from "Danger Ahoy"! Note that this is the comic strip version of the Sea Hag. The facial design of the ol' sea witch has changed since her first appearance in the "Thimble Theatre" comic strip in 1929. Pictured is the facial design that most people are familiar with.

Swee'pea ate the spinach to lend Popeye a hand from "Queen Olive Oyl", a 1973 Big Little Book adventure.

The last page to the Popeye comic book published in London by L. MILLER & CO. (1959). This book contained daily strip reprints by Tom Sims & Bill (also known as Bela) Zaboly from 1954.

Some Spinach For Popeye

Pictured are selected pages from Popeye Coloring Book #2834 (1959) by THE SAMUEL LOWE CO., Popeye Coloring Book #2834 (1961) by THE SAMUEL LOWE CO. & Popeye Coloring Book #1833-40 (1981) published by GOLDEN BOOKS.

Popeye is quite a fighter.

Art work was illustrated by Bill Zaboly, Bud Sagendorf, Artists from Paramount Cartoon Studios and illstrators from WHITMAN PUBLISHING CO.

Pictured are illustrations from a Popeye Color-By-Numbers Book by THE SAMUEL LOWE CO. from 1964 featuring drawings of the comic strip version of Popeye, one of Popeye's nephews, Wimpy, Eugene the Jeep, The Famous Studios version of Olive Oyl, Alice the Goon and despite the fact he's holding a sailor's hat, the King Features TV-cartoon version of Brutus!

Popeye Activity Books

82828

34567
82828
36457
81290

Which number is the biggest?

Pictured are illustrations from a Popeye Activity Pad (1982) published by MERRIGOLD PRESS. Illustrations include the comic strip versions of Popeye, Olive, Swee'pea (called Sweetpea), Brutus, Poopdeck Pappy, Eugene the Jeep, O.G. WottaSnozzle & Sappo (from the "Sappo" comic strip) and a drawing of Popeye wearing holsters based on how the sailor appeared in the Hanna Barbera-produced Popeye cartoons of 1978-83. Also featured is an illustration of Olive dancing with Bluto which is also based on the Hanna Barbera cartoon designs.

There are five things that are different between these pictures. Can you find them?

Match each hat to its look-alike in the pictures.

Can Olive find Sweet Pea?

ASSORTED POPEYE CARDS & STICKERS

A series of Popeye cards which were originally part of a candy package by PRIMROSE SWEETS manufactured in London. The pictured set it from the 4th Series and probably from the early 1960's. Value of a complete set is $25.00-$30.00. Courtesy of Gary Matheson

Pictured are several Popeye Valentine Day Cards produced in 1983 and featuring the comic strip designs of the Popeye cast. Value: $3.00 for a boxed set

Also pictured is a Popeye vending machine sticker used in bubble gum machines. Popeye's face is based on the King Features TV-version (note the large-sized pipe and the white around his black pupil). Also featured on this sticker are "The Little King" & "Felix the Cat". Value: $18.00-$20.00

A series of Popeye vending machine stickers by STUCK ON STICKERS (1987) featuring illustrations by Bud Sagendorf and George Wildman. Value: $1.00-$2.00 per sticker

A Popeye Get Well Card by NORCROSS (1970's).

DOLLS/PUPPETS/FIGURES

Popeye dolls, handpuppets and various kind of figures have been produced since the sailor's creation in 1929. Thanks to the success of the Fleischer/Famous Studios cartoons on television, more and more Popeye dolls were appearing in department stores. GUND was a leading manufacturer of cartoon character handpuppets and dolls during the 1950's-1960's. GUND produced Popeye, Olive Oyl, Wimpy, Swee'pea and Brutus handpuppets. They also produced several Popeye dolls featuring the sailor's head on various style bodies. For example, one of their Popeye dolls had the sailor's head stiched on a furry bunny rabbit body.

The DAKIN Co. manufactured well-designed Popeye and Olive Oyl moveable dolls during the late 1960's-1970's. Medium size figures were sold in boxes at first and later DAKIN Popeye and Olive figures were sold in totebags. DAKIN used the King Features TV cartoon version of Popeye's face while dressing the sailor in his comic strip style costume.

Recently, PRESENTS, a division of Hamilton Gifts, has produced Popeye dolls in various sizes based on the comic strip cast. Popeye, Olive Oyl, Swee'pea, Wimpy, Poopdeck Pappy, Eugene the Jeep, Brutus and The Sea Hag have all been produced in doll form. These dolls were manufactured with the collector's market in mind as all feature excellent craftsmanship and fine detail. Each doll comes with a background history of the character.

Popeye doll (large size with stand) by PRESENTS (1985). This is a well-crafted doll based on the comic strip version of Popeye. The costuming is of excellent detail. Value: $30.00

Olive Oyl doll (large size) by PRESENTS (1985). This doll is a well-crafted figure with black yarn like hair and excellent costuming design. Value: $30.00

The Sea Hag (large size) by PRESENTS (1985). The only doll, to the best of my knowledge, ever produced of the Sea Hag. Based on the comic strip version and made of excellent quality material. Value: $30.00

Wimpy (large size) by PRESENTS (1985). A well-crafted and costumed doll based on the comic strip version of the hamburger moocher. Value: $30.00

Swee'pea (large size) by PRESENTS (1985). A well-crafted and costumed doll based on the comic strip design by Swee'pea. Value: $15.00

Popeye (medium size) by PRESENTS (1985). A well-crafted and costumed Popeye doll. Value: $15.00

Wimpy (medium size) by PRESENTS (1985). A well-crafted and costumed figure of Wimpy, complete with hamburger. Value: $15.00

Brutus (medium size) by PRESENTS (1985). A well-crafted and fine detailed costume doll of the comic strip version of Brutus. Value: $15.00

Popeye handpuppet (in its original box) by GUND (1960's). The Popeye handpuppet had a squeeze device underneath its cloth body which made it "squeek" when pressed. Value (in original box): $45.00

Popeye handpuppet by GUND (1960's). A Popeye head on a cloth body decorated with little ships. Value: $20.00-$25.00

Wimpy handpuppet by GUND (1960's). A Wimpy head on a cloth body. Value: $20.00

Swee'pea handpuppet by GUND (1960's). A Swee'pea head (in a bonnet) with a cloth body decorated with baby lambs. Value: $20.00

Popeye handpuppet by GUND (1960's). A Popeye head on a Popeye comic strip costume illustrated body.
Value: $20.00

Olive Oyl handpuppet by GUND (1960's). A Olive Oyl head (based on the Famous Studios/King Features
TV-cartoons design-note the hairdo) on a comic strip costume illustrated body. Value: $20.00

Popeye rubber figure by BEN COOPER (1974). A rubber figure of the comic strip design of Popeye. Value: $16.00

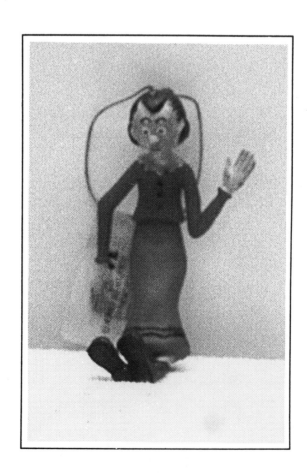

Olive Oyl rubber figure by BEN COOPER (1974). A rubber figure of Olive Oyl. Value: $16.00

Popeye doll by UNEEDA (1979). A soft vinyl doll of Popeye. The doll seems short compared to the Olive Oyl doll. Value: $7.00

Olive Oyl doll by UNEEDA (1980). A figure of Olive in removable clothing with fine costuming detail. Value: $7.00

Popeye doll by ETONE INTERNATIONAL (1983). Value: $5.00

Popeye rubber figure by COMBEX in England (1960's). A small rubber figure of Popeye holding a can of spinach. Cute design! Value: $20.00

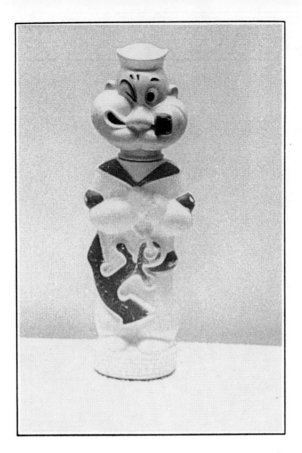

Popeye Soaky by COLGATE (1960's). A soap container in the shape of Popeye based on the King Features TV cartoon version of the sailor. Value: $18.00-$20.00

Popeye Soap Container by WOOLFOAM CORP/PLACON (1960's). Popeye shaped soap container based on the King Features TV cartoon design of the spinach eater. Value: $18.00-$20.00

Brutus Soaky by COLGATE (1960's). A soap container in the shape of Popeye's rival. Though Brutus is wearing a striped shirt and Captain's hat, his facial design is based on the King Features TV cartoons of 1960-61. Value: $18.00-$20.00

Popeye Tricky Walker by JAYMAR INC. (mid-1960's). Popeye's character design is based on the 1960-61 King Features TV-cartoon version. Value: $20.00

DIRECTIONS

Hold toy by ring; allow plastic body to drop and come to rest on a smooth surface. Now lower ring slowly and toy will scoot in any direction. Pump string up and down and the Tricky Walker will scamper about.

© KING FEATURES SYNDICATE INC.
JAYMAR SPECIALTY CO.—AUTHORIZED USER

The directions seen on the Popeye Tricky Walker featuring an illustration of the Popeye toy based on the King Features TV-cartoon version.

Olive and Swee'pea rubber stand figure by CRIBMATES (1979). The comic strip versions of Olive Oyl and Swee'pea were used for this figure.

A Popeye doll manufactured in 1983 by a woman in the final years of her life and sold in a store in Lexington, MA. My parents bought this for me for Christmas in 1983 and while it wasn't produced by an established manufacturer it is one of my prized possessions. A lot of love went into the making of this Popeye doll and I'm glad it has found a home in my house. One-of-a-Kind.

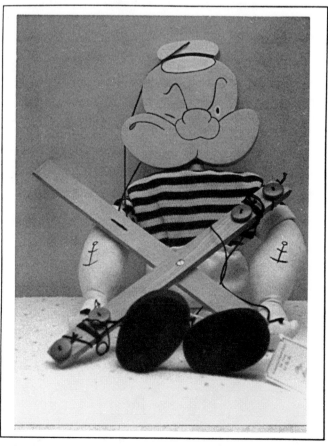

Popeye Marionette by JOAN (1987). An original crafted wooden marionette of Popeye. Value: $5.00

Popeye little figure & Olive Oyl little figure by ITI HAWAII INC. (1980's). Value: $5.00 each

Popeye and Brutus Jump-Ups by IMPERIAL TOY CO. (1979). Value: $3.00 each

Popeye Santa ornament (box) by PRESENTS (1987).

Popeye Santa ornament figure by PRESENTS (1987). Value: $4.00

Popeye ceramic figure by PRESENTS (1989). Value: $2.95

Olive ceramic figure by PRESENTS (1989). Value: $2.95

Swee'pea ceramic figure by PRESENTS (1989). Value: $2.95

Brutus ceramic figure by PRESENTS (1989). Value: $2.95

Popeye talking handpuppet by MATTEL (1968). A talking Popeye handpuppet featuring the voice of Jack Mercer, Popeye's cartoon voice. A child could use the removable pipe to blow bubbles. Value: $35.00-$40.00

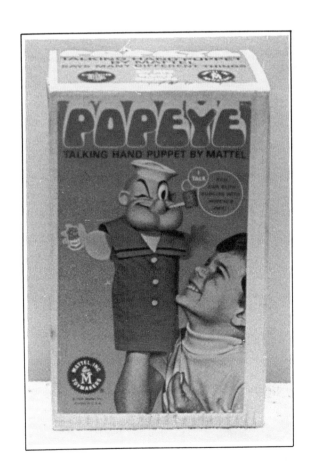

Box to Mattel's Popeye talking handpuppet.

Wimpy ceramic figure by PRESENTS (1989). Value: $2.95

The back of the box to Mattel's Popeye handpuppet gave instructions on how to hear the doll talk.

Popeye money bank by SPARDOSE-TIRELIRE (box). The box featured the "Popeye-Sixty Years" logo.

Popeye money bank (figure) by SPARDOSE-TIRELIRE (1988). This bank was purchased in Europe and based on the comic strip version of Popeye. Courtesy of Bob Cate. Value: $2.00

Popeye doll by DAKIN (late 1960's). Billed as part of Dakin's TV's Cartoon Theatre. Value: $10.00-$15.00

Olive Oyl doll by DAKIN (late 1960's). Billed as part of Dakin's TV's Cartoon Theatre. The Olive Oyl doll design is based on the King Features TV-cartoons of 1960-61. Value: $10.00-$15.00

Popeye and Olive long-shaped bendables by BRONCO CO. (1978). Value: $5.00 each

Popeye bendable figure by JESCO (1988). A poseable figure of Popeye featuring a "Popeye-Sixty Years" logo at bottom of package. Value: $3.99

Olive Oyl bendable figure by JESCO (1988). A poseable figure of Olive featuring a "Popeye-Sixty Years" logo at the bottom of the package. Value: $3.99

Popeye soft doll manufacturer unknown (1960's). This doll was given to consumers as part of a Puff White Rice cereal promotion.

Popeye Laytex dog toy (1980's).

Brutus Laytex dog toy (1980's) - featuring the comic strip version of Brutus.

Popeye moveable figure by KOHNER BROTHERS (1960's). A Popeye figure whose arms and waist move, when you press the base of the toy. Popeye's character design is based on the King Features TV cartoons. When my friend Danny, a non-toy collector, saw this piece in my collection he exclaimed, "Oh . . I remember this!" This proves that even if a person is not an avid toy collector you can recall memories from your childhood just by catching a glimpse of an old toy. Value: $5.00-$8.00

Olive moveable figure by KOHNER BROTHERS (1960's). A Olive Oyl figure whose arms and waist move, when you press the base of the toy. Olive's character design is based on the King Feaures TV-cartoon version. Value: $5.00-$8.00

Popeye doll by JOAN (1988). A soft-style doll of Popeye based on the King Features TV-cartoon version of the character. I had sent the designer of this doll photos of the 1960-61 TV-Popeye to use as reference material. One-of-a-Kind!

Wimpy's Kitchen, Cook Catch-All manufacturer unknown but produced during the 1980's. A ceramic figure of Wimpy, which is used to store kitchen gadgets. My brother, Dom, won this by playing ski-ball at an arcade. A Popeye figure was also available but I chose Wimpy because he looked better . . . one of the rare times I'd choose the moocher over the spinach-eater. Value: $5.00-$8.00

LAKESIDE'S SUPERFLEX POPEYE

One holiday season I had badly wanted a Lakeside Super-Flex Popeye bendable figure, produced in 1967, for Christmas. I had received alot of presents but no bendable Popeye! I recall my mother tucking me in bed Christmas night and asking if I got everything I wanted. I didn't want to hurt her feelings so I muttered a quiet 'yes'. A couple of days later my mom and I went to visit a friend. As we were leaving, my mom's friend handed me a brown paper bag and said she thought I might like this. I opened the bag and sure enough it was the Popeye bendable figure! Popeye was in a light blue sailor's uniform and his visual design was based on the 1960-61 King Features TV-cartoons. Like every Popeye toy I had as a child, I usually played with them to death so the bendable figure didn't stay healthy for long. Despite its quick demise I have always cherished the memory of that holiday season and the surprise I received after Christmas!

MASKS/COSTUME COLLECTIBLES

What Santa Claus is to Christmas, costumes and masks are to Halloween. For decades children have dressed up like their favorite cartoon characters and knocked on doors asking for goodies. Popeye masks/costumes have been available since the 1930's. A few years ago, I was passing out candy while wearing a Popeye T-shirt. One little girl who was no more than four years of age, came to my door wearing a Popeye mask and costume. As soon as our eyes met, we pointed at each other's clothing and shouted, "POPEYE"! It was a funny moment concerning a collectible that will no doubt continue to delight children for decades to come.

Popeye Costume & Mask by COLLEGEVILLE COSTUMES (1950's). The boxed set of the Popeye mask/costume. Sold in the box the value is $45.00.

Popeye Mask & Costume by COLLEGEVILLE COSTUMES (1950's). The Popeye mask is based on comic strip artist Bill Zaboly's version of the sailor. Their is an anchor drawn on the sailor's cap. The "Popeye" logo is on the costume and a blue bonnet is included.

Popeye Mask & Costume by COLLEGEVILLE COSTUMES (1960's-1970's). Though it's pictured in the box, you can see that Popeye has white around the pupil of his eye and a big pipe. These are two signs that the facial design of the sailor is based on the King Features TV-cartoons of 1960-1961. This mask had several different costume designs to go along with it. They included, Popeye in his white sailor's suit popping out of a television set & the comic strip version of Popeye holding a can of spinach. Value: $10.00-$20.00

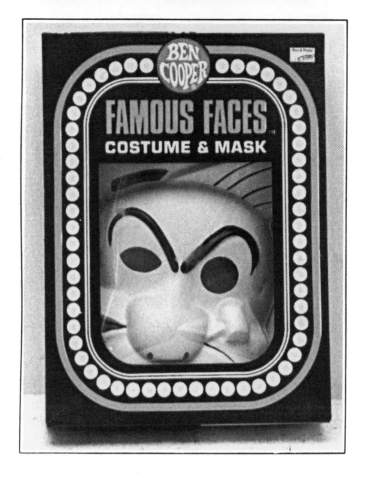

Popeye Mask & Costume by COLLEGEVILLE COSTUMES (late 1980's). The boxed set is valued at $4.00.

Popeye Mask & Costume by COLLEGEVILLE COSTUMES (late 1980's). The Popeye mask is based on Bud Sagendorf's version of the comic strip sailor and the costume featured a big picture of Popeye's face in the center.

BLISTER PACK TOYS

Blister pack toys are the products you would usually find hanging on the rack of a spinning turn-style in a supermarket or drugstore. Popeye blister pack products have populated stores for years with two companies providing much of the merchandise during the 1970's and 1980's; JA-RU & LARAMI.

However, many of the blister pack toys would only use the "Popeye" name and illustrations to help sell the product. Popeye, himself, would usually have nothing to do with the product. For example, "Popeye's Pool Table" would feature the sailor's name and face but the little toy pool table would have nothing to do with the spinach-eater. Often times tiny decals of Popeye would be placed on the toys to provide some linkage.

Today, blister pack toys are still being sold and many feature the "Popeye & Son" (from the 1987-88 cartoon series) name and characters. A word of warning to collectors of blister pack items; I have run across dealers who are selling items you can still buy for a $1.99 at your local supermakret for $20.00-$25.00. Be very inquisitive before purchasing any of these kind of items and this should be a general rule before purchasing any kind of cartoon/comic strip charcter collectible.

Popeye Glo-Whistle by HELM TOYS (1984). A whistle that lights up when you blow into it. Value: $2.50

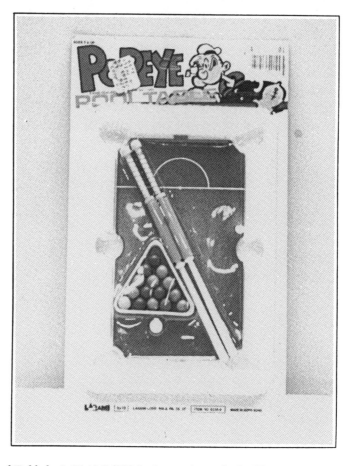

Popeye Pool Table by LARAMI (1984). A toy using only the "Popeye" name. Value: $1.39

Popeye Tube-A-Loonies by LARAMI (1981). You could blow colorful balloons with the material in this toy. Value: $1.00

Popeye Tube-A-Loonies by LARAMI (1983). A set of 5 tubes of Tube-A-Loonies mixture to create colorful balloons! Value: $2.00

Popeye Hauling and Construction Set by TOYS FOR ALL SEASONS (1970's). Plastic trucks, wheels and lil' construction material with small Popeye decals. Value: $2.00

Popeye Boat Bubble Blower by LARAMI (1984). Popeye bubble liquid and a Popeye figure in a lil' boat came in this package. Value: $2.00

Popeye and Son Pop Maker by JA-RU (1987). You could make you own frozen pops with the plastic containers. Based on the "Popeye and Son" cartoon series. Value: $1.69

Popeye Shaving Kit by LARAMI (1979). Plastic shaving toys featuring a Popeye decal on the little cup. Value: $2.00

Popeye and Son Wood Slate by JA-RU (1987). A small blackboard and chalk based on the "Popeye and Son" cartoon series. Value: $2.99

Popeye Magnets by LARAMI (1984. A large and small magnet toy using only the "Popeye" name. Value: $1.09

Popeye Doodle Ball by JA-RU (1981). Use the magnetic wand to create drawings from the little black balls.
Value: $2.00

Popeye Party Game by UNIQUE IND. (1980). This packaged set contained ideas on how to have a party featuring Popeye-related games. Also enclosed were "Popeye fun Booklets" featuring comic strip reprints. Value: 1.00

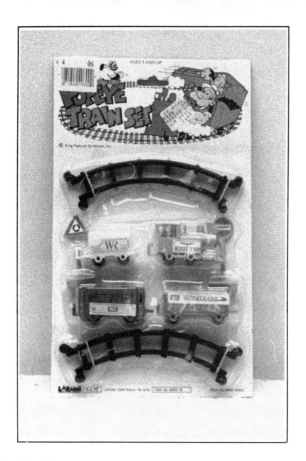

Popeye Train Set by LARAMI (1980's). A toy using only the "Popeye" name. This toy is of more recent vintage, yet, some dealers charge at least $10.00 for this collectible. BUYER BEWARE! Value: $1.69

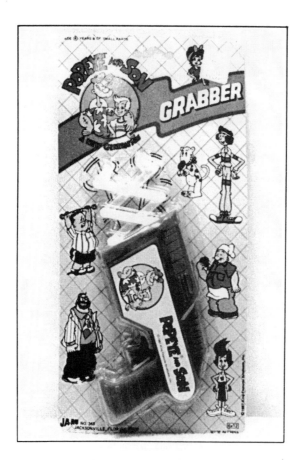

Popeye and Son Grabber by JA-RU (1987). A toy based on the "Popeye and Son" cartoon series. The package features illustrations of Wimpy's nephew, Bluto, The Jeep, Olive, Wimpy and Woody as they appeared in the "Popeye & Son" cartoons. Value: $2.00

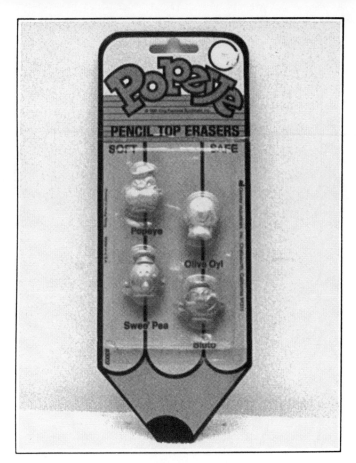

Popeye Pencil Top Erasers by DIENER INDUSTRIES (1981). Erasers were Popeye, Olive, Swee'pea and Bluto (instead of being called Brutus which ost collectibles featuring the bully were at this time). Value: $1.00-$2.00

Popeye's Pipe by CONTINENTAL PLASTICS/HARMONY TOYS (1980). Value: $2.00-$5.00

Small Popeye Bendable figure by AMSCAN (1980)

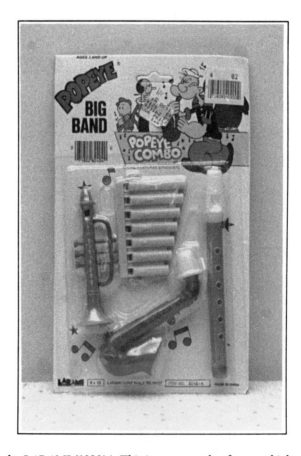

Popeye Big Band Combo by LARAMI (1980's). *This is an example of a toy which only used the Popeye name and character's on the package. The characters themselves have nothing to do with the acutal product. Value: $2.00*

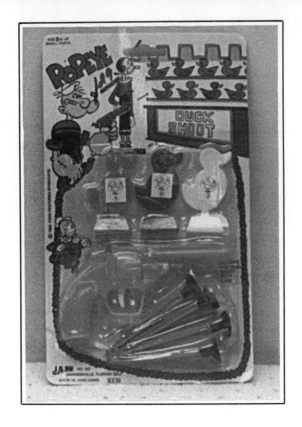

Popeye Duck Shoot by JA-RU (1983). A Popeye target game featuring a plastic gun, darts and ducks. Value: $1.29

Popeye Pen by N.J. CROCE CO. (1985). A pen with a Popeye body on the upper part of the writing instrument. The pens also featured Wimpy, Olive Oyl and Swee'pea. Value: $2.00

Olive Oyl Bike Boobers (1960's) manufacturer unknown. A plastic figure of Olive attached to a spring where it could be place on a child's bike's steering handle. Olive Oyl's visual design is based on the King Features TV-cartoons. Value: $30.00

Popeye Bike Bobbers (1960's) manufacturer unknown. A plastic figure of Popeye attached to a spring which could be placed on a child's bike's steering handles. The visual design of Popeye is based on the King Features TV cartoons. Value: $30.00

Popeye Puzzle by ROALEX CO. (1950's-sold till late 1970's) A small puzzle featuring the 1950's comic strip designs of the Popeye cast. The artwork on the card was done by Popeye comic strip artist, Bill Zaboly. Swee'pea is wearing his sailor's uniform that he wore in the comic strip from the mid-1950's to 1959. Value: $16.00

Popey Harmonica by LARAMI (1980's). A harmonica with the "Popeye" logo printed on it. Value: $1.39

Popeye Erasers by DIENER INDUSTRIES (1981). Rubber eraser figures of Popeye and Brutus (comic strip version). Value: $1.00

Popeye Viewmaster Showbeam Cartridge (1982). A Popeye adventure you put in Viewmaster's Showbeam Projector. Value: $3.69

Popeye BendiFace by LAKESIDE (1968). A soft foam rubber facial design of Popeye children could squeeze and make funny faces. Popeye's facial design is based on the King Features TV-cartoon version of 1960-61. Value: $12.00

CORGI Olive Oyl in a plane (1980). A little plastic figure of Olive Oyl in a plane with Popeye and Swee'pea decals on the plane's wings. Value: $2.00

Popeye Ring Toss by HAPPY-MATES (1980). A cardboard figure of the comic strip version of Popeye eating a can of spinach. You could toss plastic rings around the figure. Value: $1.49

Official Popeye Gumball Dispenser by SUPERIOR TOY (1983). Value: $2.00

Popeye stickers (19180's) manufacturer unknown though the pack is labled "Happy Stickers . . . made in Taiwan".

Popey Wood Slate by JA-RU (1983). A blackborad with chalk featuring the comic strip version of Popeye. Value: $2.00

Popeye Pop-Up Wash Cloth by MAGICAL MYSTERY PRODUCTS (1987) An expandable 13" x 13" wash cloth featuring an illustration of Popeye saying "I yam what I yam an' tha's all I yam". It's interesting to note that along with the standard "King Features Syndicate" copyright notice on these wash cloths, "Fleischer Studios" is also mentioned as being part of the copyright holder. Fleishcher Studios proded the original Popeye theatre cartoons from 1933-1942. This is the only collectible that I've seen featuring "Fleischer Studios" as part of the copyright information. Value: $2.00

Popeye Sand Set by PEER PRODUCTIONS (1950's). You could mold Popeye and Olive faces into the sand and use the little plastic shovel. Value: $10.00

CARTOONIST STAMP SET

A few years back I visited a store which sold collectible toys in Melrose, MA called "Sweet's Stuff". I was on my never-ending search for Popeye collectibles. While I was going through a pile of old toys I noticed a stamp set decorated with illustrations of Huckleberry Hound, Yogi Bear and Top Cat. I recall having a Popeye stamp set when I was growing up which featured stamps of Popeye, Olive Oyl, J. Wellington, Rough House and Geezil. Also included in the set were Felix the Cat, Felix's nephews, Felix's magic bag and The Professor. Since I saw cartoon characters from the studio of Hanna Barbera on this stamp set I didn't think to give it another look. As I was preparing to leave the store, however, I had the urge to look at the stamp set once again. As I looked at the actual stamps in the package, I noticed Greezil, my heart jumped, then I spotted Rough House, I suddenly became excited. The other stamps in this set were Popeye, Olive Oyl and the Felix the Cat character stamps. Though Hanna Barbera characters were pictured on the package, the set contained the Popeye stamps I had as a child. I quickly paid for the set and walked out of the store clutching another childhood memory to my chest.

POPEYE HOME MOVIES & RECORDS

During the 1970's, Atlas Films produced a number of Popeye Super 8 movie films with footage taken directly from Fleischer, Famous Studios and King Features TV-cartoons. With the event of being able to tape a feature film or cartoon with a VCR, the production of these home movies came to a halt. Now these Popeye films have become rare collectibles.

Children's records are not being produced very much today but Popeye flourished in this market. Many Popeye children's recordings featured Popeye's cartoon voice, Jack Mercer and Olive Oyl's, Mae Questel. Wonderland Records, Capitol Records and Peter Pan Records were among the outfits producing Popeye material. The majority of the art work on the record sleeves featured the comic strip designs of the Popeye cast. Though children's records are not being produced as much as they were a decade ago, many stores still carry Popeye material produced by Peter Pan during the 1970's and 1980's.

Kiddie Movies, "Popeye in Best of Popeye" by ATLAS FILMS. 8MM movie featuring scenes from Popeye cartoons produced by Fleischer Studios. This was but one in a series of Popeye Kiddie Movies produced by ATLAS FILMS during the 1970's. The picture of Popeye on the box is based on the animated-Fleischer version of the sailor man. Value: $8.00-$10.00

Popeye Kiddie Movies by ATLAS FILMS (1970's). This Super 8 movie is called "Spinachville" and taken from a Fleischer Popeye cartoon. Value: $8.00-$10.00

233

Popeye Kiddie Movie, "Popeye in Private Eye" by ATLAS FILMS (1970's). Billed on the box as a "Featurette" with footage made up from the 1954 Famous Studios cartoon, "Private Eye Popeye".
Value: $8.00-$10.00

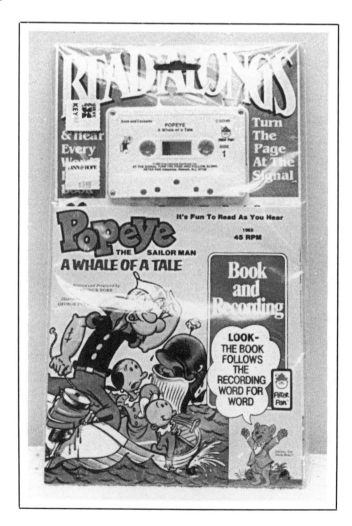

Popeye-"A Whale of A Tale-Read Alongs" by Peter Pan (1969/1983). You could listen to the 1983 produced cassette tape and read along with the 1969 illustrated book. Value: $3.49

Popeye-"Oyle On Troubled Waters" by Peter Pan (1975). You could listen to the 1983 cassette tape and read along with the 1975 Popeye adventure. Value: $3.49

Popeye Record by Peter Pan (1964) featuring the stories, "Skin Divers", "Flea's A Crowd". Both stories were based on 1960 King Features TV cartoons. Value: $7.00

Selected pages from the 1969 Popeye Book and Record adventure, "A Whale of A Tale". The artwork was illustrated by George Peed who designed the animated cartoon characters who appeared in "The Mighty Hercules" series of the 1960's.

Suddenly the engine sputtered and then stopped.
"What's wrong, Popeye?"
"We is outta gas!—Hmmm, just what I thought—
a hole in the gas tank—Hey! The oars are gone too! I smells
somethin' fishy, what it goes by the name of Brutus!"
Olive Oyl was worried. "What'll we do, Popeye?
It will be dark soon!"

"Whoa now!" said Popeye. "Don't give up the ship!
I got just what yer needs—my super-special, super-duper,
triple power spinach in the super-size can. Here—
try some of this—ole buddy!"

And Mopey gobbled up the spinach, can and all.
"Mmmmmm—oh yeah! I kin feel the power surgin' through
me head muskles n' me flipper muskles n' me tail muskles!
Hold on, anybody—here we goes!"

And straining every muscle in his powerful body,
Mopey rammed his way forward.

"Whee, we're moving!" shouted Swee'pea.

Selected pages from the 1975 Popeye Book and Record adventure, "Oyle On Troubled Waters" illustrated by Mary Jane Fahey.

Record sleeve to a Popeye record by Peter Pan (1960). Value of the record sleeve: $20.00

3 complete Little Golden Records on 45 R.P.M. EP featuring Bugs Bunny, Mighty Mouse and "I'm Popeye the Sailor Man" theme song. Featuring Mitch Miller, The Sandpipers and The Terrytooners! Printed by EP Golden Records (late 1950's). Value: $20.00

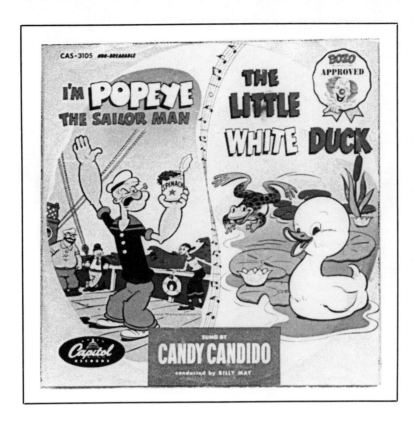

Capitol Records "I'm Popeye the Sailor Man" theme song sung by Candy Candido and "The Little White Duck". "A Bozo Approved" record (Bozo the Clown was the symbol for Capitol records for several children's records) (late 1950's). Value: $15.00-$20.00

Peter Pan "Popeye the Sailor Man" — musical stories from original TV scripts - narrated by Harry F. Welch. "Skin Divers", "Jeep, Jeep", "Where There Is A Will" & "Fleas A Crowd". All of the stories on this 1976 album are based on King Features TV-cartoon scripts from 1960. Value: $5.00

Peter Pan "Popeye the Sailor Man - 4 Exciting Stories". Featured on this 1970's album are the stories, "Moon Struck", "Pollution Solution", "Oyle On Troubled Waters" & "A Child Shall Lead Them". Value: $5.00

Peter Pan "Popeye - This Album Contains 4 Stories". Stories from this 1980's album include "Popeye in the Movies", "Spinach on the Spanish Main", "Gold Fever" & "Who's Afraid of a U.F.O." Value: $3.00

Popeye lifting a horse is from the back of "Popeye - This Album Contains 4 Stories" by Peter Pan records.

Popeye Color, Listen, Read and Learn kit by Peter Pan. This 1983 set contained a cassette tape of the story "A Whale of A Tale" along with a coloring book and crayons. Value: $4.00

Wonderland Records "Popeye the Sailor Man and his Friends". This 1974 album featured the animated cartoon voices of both Popeye and Olive Oyl, Jack Mercer and Mae Questel. Songs on this album were "I'm Popeye the Sailor Man", "Popeye in Cartoon-Land", "Strolling Through the Park", "Help! Help" and I Had a Hamburger Dream", "Home On the Range", "Television Night", "Never Pick A Fight", "Every State is a Great State", "Take Me Out to the Ball Game", "The Emperor of Japan", "A Game for a Rainy Day" & "Why Do You Answer a Question With a Question?". Value: $7.00-$10.00

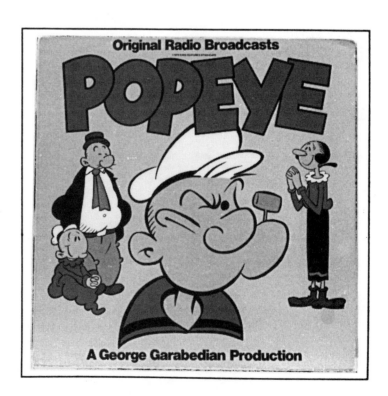

Original radio broadcasts "Popeye" - a George Garabedian Production. This album featured stories which were first heard on the 1930's Popeye radio show. This album was produced in 1976. Value: $3.00

The back of George Garabedian's Popeye radio story album featured a "Thimble Theatre starring Popeye" strip.

Nostalgia Lane "Popeye - Original Radio Broadcast". Featured on this album were "Popeye and the Runaway Trolley", "Popeye and Who's Who at the Zoo", "Popeye, Geranium & The Giant" and "Popeye Meets Robin Hood". A 1976 album. Value: $3.00

Peter Pan "Popeye and Friends" Christmas stories. This 1977 album featured "Popeye's cartoon voice, Jack Mercer in "4 Exciting Christmas Stories", "Christmas Pie", "Pearl Burgers", "Deck the Halls" & "Santa Popeye". Value: $3.00

The back of Peter Pan's Popeye Christmas album featured illustrations based on the stories heard on the album.

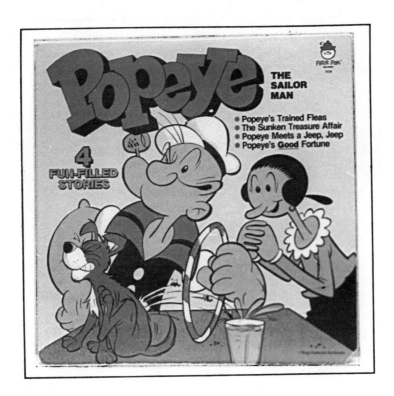

Peter Pan "Popeye the Sailor Man - 4 Fun Filled Stories", "Popeye's Trained Fleas", "The Sunken Treasure Affair", "Popeye Meets A Jeep-Jeep" & "Popeye's Good Fortune". A 1980 album. Value: $3.00

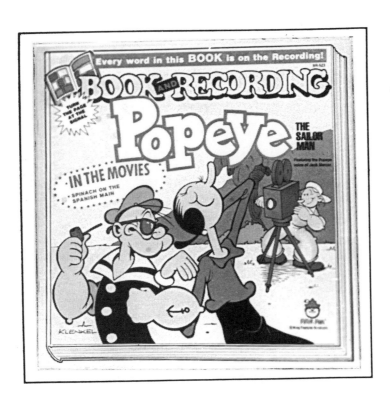

Peter Pan "Popeye the Sailor Man - Book & Recording". The album cover opened like a book which contained comic book style illustrations based on the two adventures heard on the album; "Popeye In the Movies" & "Spinach On the Spanish Main". A 1980's album. Value: $3.00

The back of Peter Pan's picture disk Popeye album produced in 1982. Featured on this record were the stories; "Popeye In the Movies", "Spinach On the Spanish Main", "Gold Fever" and "Who's Afraid of a UFO". Value: $3.00

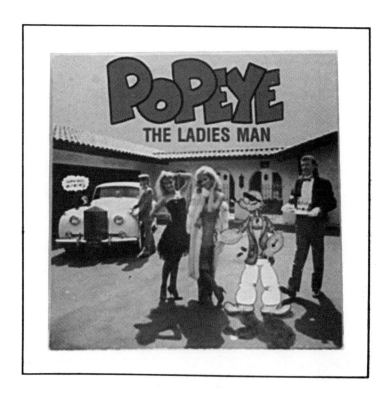

PanaRecord International's "Popeye the Ladies Man". This was a cleverly written song which turned Popeye into a Don Johnson type swinger! This album featured the voice work of Jerry LoBozzo, who has performed Popeye's voice for a few TV-commercials in recent years. Value: $10.00

POPEYE ON VIDEO

With the popularity of VCR's, Popeye films by Fleischer Studios, Famous Studios and King Features Syndicate have found new homes on video tapes produced by various companies. The three color, 20-minute Popeye films produced by Fleischer Studios; "Popeye Meets Ali Baba's Forty Thieves" (1937) and "Alladin and His Wonderful Lamp" (1939) have appeared on several different tapes. Many Famous Studios Popeye cartoons have appeared as well as King Features Syndicate's TV-cartoons. The King Features cartoons have been packaged as theme-tapes; "Popeye Out West", "Popeye and Friends In Outer Space" and "Travelin' On About Travel" are a few examples. "Beetle Bailey", "Snuffy Smith", "Krazy Kat" & "Cool McCool" cartoons, all produced by King Features Syndicate during the 1960's, appear on the Popeye-theme tapes.

There are no values listed for each tape because several still are sold in stores today. The Quality of each really depends upon the company who produced it and the shape of the print the Popeye cartoon was transferred from.

Popeye-Sinbad the Sailor by Troy Gold. The "Sinbad" cartoon is featured on this tape and so are "Ancient History" (1953) and "Floor Flusher" (1954).

Cartoon Favorites; Popeye by Trans-Atlantic Video. Features "Popeye the Sailor Meets Sinbad the Sailor" (1936) and the black & white Fleischer Studios cartoon, "Li'l Swee'pea" (1936).

The Adventures of Popeye Vol. III by Superstar Cartoon Video. Features all Famous Studios films; "Popeye For President" (1956), "Assault & Flattery" (1956), "Fright to the Finish" (1954) and "Bride & Gloom" (1954).

Popeye by Kids Flicks. Features "Popeye the Sailor Meets Sinbad the Sailor" (1936) and "Popeye Meets Ali Baba's Forty Thieves" (1937).

Popeye the Sailor-Travelin' On by Interglobal Video from Canada. The "Sinbad", "Alladin" and "Ali Baba" films are all strung together on this tape.

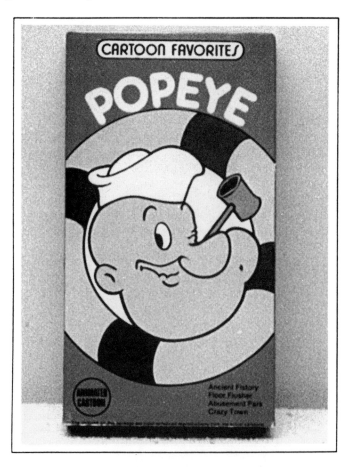

Cartoon Favorites; Popeye by Trans-Atlantic Video. Features all Famous Studios films; "Ancient History" (1953), "Floor Flushers" (1954), "Amusement Park" (1947) and a non-Popeye cartoon by Famous Studios "Crazy Town".

Popeye-Popeye Meets Ali Baba by Troy Gold. The "Ali Baba" cartoon is featured on this tape and Amusement Park" (1947).

The Adventures of Popeye Vol V by Superstar Cartoon Video. Featured on this tape are all Famous Studios films, "Gopher Spinach" (1954), "Out to Punch" (1956), "Parlez Voo Woo" (1956) and "A Haul In One" (1956).

INTRODUCE YOUR FRIENDS TO...

POPEYE, THE COLLECTIBLE!

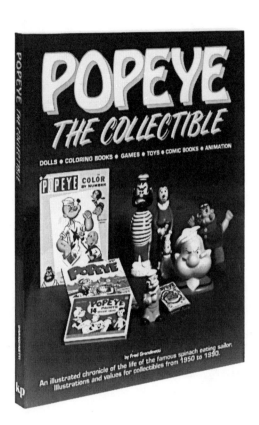

THE FIRST BOOK-LENGTH GUIDE TO POPEYE COLLECTIBLES...

Including:
- **Four Decades of Coverage** - thoroughly catalogs Popeye collectibles from the 1950's through the 1980's, to aid beginning and veteran collectors alike!
- **A Historical Overview** - gives you valuable insights into Popeye's popularity throughout the decades!
- **Comic Strip/Film Appearances** - helps you build your collection with the fundamental ingredients of a total Popeye library!
- **Individual Sections in Detail** - provides you with special coverage of coloring books. Big Little books, animation collectibles, comic books, and toys, to make your collection complete!
- **Each Item Priced in Today's Dollars** - helps you determine the true value of all the Popeye collectibles you now own or want to someday!

Special Low First-Edition Price... **$19.95** plus $2.50 shipping

---

Give the first POPEYE collector's guide ever published!

Return coupon with proper remittance to:

Krause Publications, Book Dept.
700 E. State St., Iola, WI 54990

( ) **YES!** Send _____ copy(ies) of POPEYE, THE COLLECTIBLE immediately at $19.95 plus $2.50 shipping for the first book, and $1.50 shipping for each additional book ordered, to the person listed below.

Foreign addresses add $5.00 per book for shipping. Payable in U.S. funds only.

Name _____

Address _____

City _____

State _____ Zip _____
KOD

Total for books $ _____

Total for shipping $ _____

Total enclosed $ _____

Our Guarantee
Examine POPEYE, THE COLLECTIBLE in your home. If you're not completely satisfied, you can return it within 10 days for a full refund, less shipping costs.

Method of Payment

( ) Check or money order (to Krause Publications)
( ) MasterCard   ( ) VISA

Credit Card No. _____

Expires: Mo. _____ Yr. _____

Signature _____

Phone (_____) _____

TELEPHONE ORDERS

MasterCard & VISA users call:
800-258-0929
Mon.-Fri., 6:30 am to 8:00 pm, CST

Wisconsin residents call:
715-445-2214
Mon.-Fri., 7:30 am to 5:30 pm, CST